Important Instruction

Students, Parents, and Teachers can use the URL or QR code provided below to access two full-length Lumos Algebra 1 practice tests, hundreds of additional practice questions, educational videos, worksheets, mobile apps, standards information and more.

URL	QR Code
Visit the URL below and place the book access code **http://www.lumoslearning.com/a/tedbooks** **Access Code: HSALG1-40825-P**	

lumos learning
Developed by Expert Teachers

High School Algebra 1 - Math Skills Mastery Lumos tedBook : Online Assessments and Practice Workbooks

Contributing Author	-	John Eaton
Contributing Author	-	Tammie Rolf
Contributing Author	-	Lauren Inzelbuch
Contributing Author	-	Karen O Brien
Contributing Author	-	Donald Woods
Contributing Author	-	Janese Mott
Contributing Author	-	Paul Spinler
Contributing Author	-	Karen Russell
Contributing Author	-	Larry Russell
Executive Producer	-	Mukunda Krishnaswamy
Designer and Illustrator	-	Sowmya R.

ISBN-10: 1-949855-01-5

ISBN-13: 978-1-949855-01-2

Printed in the United States of America

For permissions and additional information contact us

Lumos Information Services, LLC
PO Box 1575, Piscataway, NJ 08855-1575
http://www.LumosLearning.com

Email: support@lumoslearning.com
Tel: (732) 384-0146
Fax: (866) 283-6471

Developed by Expert Teachers

Table of Contents

Online Program Benefits

Students*

- Two full-length Lumos Algebra-1 practice tests
- Rigorous Standards Practice
- Technology-enhanced item types practice
- Additional learning resources such as videos and apps

Parents*

- You can review your student's online work by login to your parent account
- Pinpoint student areas of difficulty
- Develop custom lessons & assignments
- Access to High-Quality Question Bank

Teachers*

- Review the online work of your students
- Get insightful student reports
- Discover standards aligned videos, apps and books through EdSearch
- Easily access standards information along with the Coherence Map
- Create and share information about your classroom or school events

* Terms and Conditions apply

URL	QR Code
Visit the URL below and place the book access code **http://www.lumoslearning.com/a/tedbooks** **Access Code: HSALG1-40825-P**	

Start using the online resources included with this book today!

Introduction

This book is designed to help students get High School Algebra 1 rehearsal along with standards aligned with rigorous skills practice. Algebra 1 is one of the credits that students will have to earn as a part of Mathematics credit requirement for High School Graduation requirements.

Unlike a traditional book, this Lumos tedBook offers two full-length practice tests both in the printed version as well as Online version. Taking these tests will not only help students get a comprehensive review of standards assessed in Algebra 1 but also become familiar with the technology-enhanced question types.

After students take the test online, educators can use the score report to assign specific lessons provided in this book.

Students will obtain a better understanding of each standard and improve on their weaknesses by practicing the content of this workbook. The lessons contain rigorous questions aligned to the state standards and substandards. Taking the time to work through the activities will afford students the ability to become proficient in each grade level standard.

How will Lumos StepUp® program help students in preparing for the end of course exams of High School Math credit programs?

The Lumos StepUp® program for High School Math courses includes

(a) Two Full-length practice tests

(b) Get realistic practice through Online Assessments. It gives students the opportunity to practice test-taking skills, familiarize with the format of the test and efficiently review the key topics. The results will help you get insights into your child's strengths and weaknesses in various content areas. These insights could be used to help your child strengthen their skills in topics where they are having difficulty. This test practice helps them improve speed and accuracy while taking the actual High School Math Assessments.

(c) StepUp® has great learning content with access to hundreds of activities and Online workbooks.

(d) Your child's work is carefully and meticulously tracked throughout the program. Easy-to-use, advanced and real-time reports will help you identify weak areas and tailor personalized learning plans for your child.

(e) The StepUp® program allows your child to prepare at a pace that is right for him or her. This student-centric approach, combined with instant feedback boosts student confidence and improves learning outcomes.

(f) StepUp® program can be accessed through a number of devices that include, PC, tablet and smart-phones and it is available 24×7. This convenience helps to enable anywhere learning.

Discover Engaging and Relevant Learning Resources

Lumos EdSearch is a safe search engine specifically designed for teachers and students. Using EdSearch, you can easily find thousands of standards-aligned learning resources such as questions, videos, lessons, worksheets and apps. Teachers can use EdSearch to create custom resource kits to perfectly match their lesson objective and assign them to one or more students in their classroom.

To access the EdSearch tool, use the search box after you log into Lumos StepUp or use the link provided below.

http://www.lumoslearning.com/a/edsearchb	

The Lumos Standards Coherence map provides information about previous level, next level and related standards. It helps educators and students visually explore learning standards. It's an effective tool to help students progress through the learning objectives. Teachers can use this tool to develop their own pacing charts and lesson plans. Educators can also use the coherence map to get deep insights into why a student is struggling in a specific learning objective.

Teachers can access the Coherence maps after logging into the StepUp Teacher Portal or use the link provided below.

http://www.lumoslearning.com/a/coherence-map	

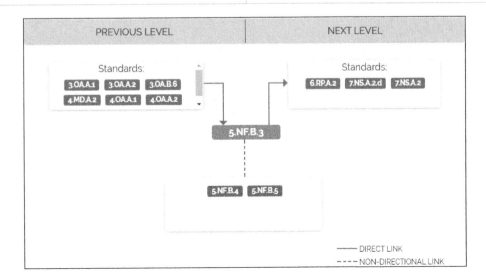

The Lumos Program is a flexible learning tool. It can be adapted to suit a student's skill level and the time available to practice before standardized tests. Here are some tips to help you use this book and the online resources effectively:

Students

- The standards in each book can be practiced in the order designed, or in the order you prefer.
- Complete all problems in each workbook.
- Take the first practice assessment online which has 2 parts in Math.
- Have open-ended questions evaluated by a teacher or parent, keeping in mind the scoring rubrics.
- Take the second practice assessment as you get close to the official test date. This will also have 2 parts in Math.
- Complete the test in a quiet place, following the test guidelines. Practice tests provide you an opportunity to improve your test taking skills and to review topics included in the test.

Parents

- Help your child use Lumos StepUp® Online Assessments by following the instructions in "Access Online Program" section.
- You can review your student's online work by login to your parent account.
- You can also conveniently access student progress report on your mobile devices by downloading the Lumos StepUp app. Please follow directions provided in "How can I Download the App?" section in Lumos StepUp® Mobile App FAQ For Parents and Teachers.

1) **The day before the test,** make sure you get a good night's sleep.

2) **On the day of the test,** be sure to eat a good hearty breakfast! Also, be sure to arrive at school on time.

3) **During the test:**

- **Read every question carefully.**

  - Do not spend too much time on any one question. Work steadily through all questions in the section.
  - Attempt all of the questions even if you are not sure of some answers.
  - If you run into a difficult question, eliminate as many choices as you can and then pick the best one from the remaining choices. Intelligent guessing will help you increase your score.
  - Also, mark the question so that if you have extra time, you can return to it after you reach the end of the section.
  - Some questions may refer to a graph, chart, or other kind of picture. Carefully review the infographics before answering the question.
  - Be sure to include explanations for your written responses and show all work.

- **While Answering TECR questions.**

  - Read the directions of each question. Some might ask you to drag something, others to select, and still others to highlight. Follow all instructions of the question (or questions if it is in multiple parts)

Here are some reminders for when you are taking the Practice Test.

To answer the questions on the test, use the directions given in the question. If you do not know the answer to a question, skip it and go on to the next question. If time permits, you may return to questions in this session only. Do your best to answer every question.

Practice Test 1

1. **What is the exponential model for the data in the table below?**

x	y
5	160
7	640

Ⓐ $y=5(2)^x$
Ⓑ $y=2(5)^x$
Ⓒ $y=10(2)^x$
Ⓓ $y=32^x$

2. **Jack purchased some shares of stock in a successful company. The graph below shows the value of the shares over time. He wants to sell the shares when their value is twice what he paid for them. During which month after Jack bought the shares are the shares double their original value?**

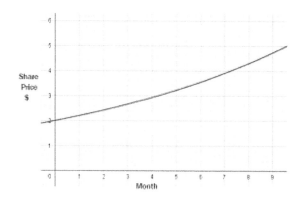

Ⓐ 6
Ⓑ 7
Ⓒ 8
Ⓓ 9

3. You don't think the absolute value symbol is needed when simplifying the expression $\sqrt[a]{n^a}$ when "a" is an even number.

You say that the result is always n .

Which example below does not support your conjecture?

(A) $\sqrt[5]{7^5} = 7$

(B) $\sqrt[4]{7^4} = 7$

(C) $\sqrt[4]{(-7^4)} = 7$

(D) $\sqrt[4]{(-7^4)} = |-7|$

4. Which of the following is a zero of the following quadratic expression ? $6x^2 - 17x - 14$

(A) -2

(B) 7

(C) $\frac{2}{3}$

(D) $-\frac{7}{2}$

(E) $\frac{7}{2}$

5. Suppose you were asked to graph $y_1 = (x+5)(x-2)$ and $y_2 = x^2 + 3x - 10$ on the same coordinate plane. What would be true about both graphs?

6. The sum of three consecutive even integers is 72.
What is the middle integer?

(A) 22

(B) 26

(C) 28

(D) 24

7. A rectangular field has a perimeter of 300m. What is the area of the field if the length of the field is twice the width of the field?

   Ⓐ 5000 m²
   Ⓑ 300 m²
   Ⓒ 5000 m
   Ⓓ 600 m²

8. Suppose the stocks of cases of bottled water on the shelves of a major grocery store follow the graph of the equation $4x+y=36$ where x is hours after the store opens and y is the number of cases on the shelves. All of the water is sold. What is the domain of the variable x?

   Ⓐ [0,6]
   Ⓑ [0,9]
   Ⓒ [0,12]
   Ⓓ [-2,9]

9. Solve for b in the formula $A=\frac{1}{2}h(B+b)$.

   Ⓐ $b = \frac{1}{2}h(B + A)$

   Ⓑ $b = \frac{1}{2}h(A + b)$

   Ⓒ $b = \frac{2A}{h} - B$

   Ⓓ $b = \frac{2A}{B} - h$

10. The amount of water that is added to a reservoir (a large lake where the water is held in by a dam) is given by the function $w(t)=t^3-t^2+100$, where w is measured in gallons and t is in days. At the same time the amount of water that is released out of the reservoir thru the dam is given by the function, $p(t)=t^3-3t^2+300$, where p is measured in gallons and t is in days. Which of the following expressions represents the difference in w(t) and p(t)?

   Ⓐ $-2t^3-4t^2-200$
   Ⓑ $2t^2-200$
   Ⓒ $-2t^3-4t^2+200$
   Ⓓ $2(t+10)(t-10)$

11. Solve: $5x+7 \geq 32$

    Ⓐ $x=5$
    Ⓑ $x \leq 5$
    Ⓒ $x \geq 5$
    Ⓓ $x > 5$

12. Solve: $4(x-5)+5=21$

    Ⓐ 8
    Ⓑ 32
    Ⓒ 9
    Ⓓ 36

13. The graph of $x-3y=-6$ is shown below.

    What do the points on the graph represent?

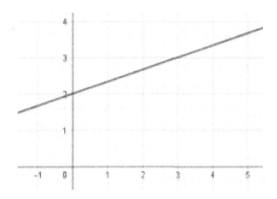

    Ⓐ **All solutions to the equation**
    Ⓑ **Restrictions on the domain**
    Ⓒ **Output values**
    Ⓓ **Input values**

14. The graph of $y=x^2-2x-8$ is shown below. What are the solutions to the curve?

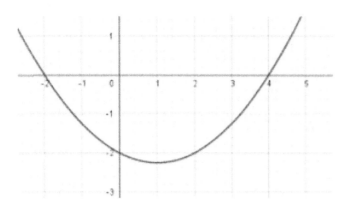

Ⓐ $x=-2,4$
Ⓑ $y=-2,4$
Ⓒ $x=-4,2$
Ⓓ $y=-4,2$

15. Which statement is true about the domain and range of a function?

Ⓐ The domain is the set of outputs, the range is the set of inputs
Ⓑ The domain is the set of inputs, the range is the set of outputs
Ⓒ The range is the set of independent variables, the domain is the set of dependent
Ⓓ The domain is the set of independent variables, the range is the also the set of independent variables

16. If $-x^2-2x<-8$, which of the following could be true about x ?

Ⓐ $-4<x<2$
Ⓑ $x<-4$
Ⓒ $x>2$
Ⓓ No solution since x^2 cannot be less than a negative number

17. For Algebra I homework, Catherine was asked to solve $5(y+1)+3=23$ **for y. She put the following on the board.**

Line 1	$5(y+1)+3=23$
Line 2	$5(y+1)=20$
Line 3	$5y+1=23$
Line 4	$5y=22$
Line 5	$\frac{5Y}{5} = \frac{22}{5}$
Line 6	$Y = \frac{22}{5}$

Which property did she make an error with when going from line 2 to line 3?

18. Function $h(x) = f(x) + g(x)$.
What is $h(x)$ **if** $f(x)=x^2-3x+9$ **and,** $g(x)=6x^2-4x-7$?

Ⓐ $h(x)=7x^2-7x+2$
Ⓑ $h(x)=7x^4-7x^2+2$
Ⓒ $h(x)=7x^2+7x+2$
Ⓓ $h(x)=7x^2+7x+16$

19. Suppose ΔABC ~ ΔDEF shown below. What is cos F?

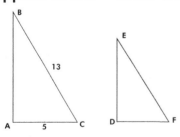

Ⓐ $\frac{13}{5}$

Ⓑ $\frac{12}{13}$

Ⓒ $\frac{13}{12}$

Ⓓ $\frac{5}{13}$

20. A classmate of yours stated that a solid line is not a good representation of an arithmetic sequence. What logical assumption is your classmate using?

   Ⓐ A line is a series of dots that represents each value of the sequence.
   Ⓑ A line has the same slope as the common difference in the sequence.
   Ⓒ An arithmetic sequence is a set of discrete values, whereas a line is a continuous set of values.
   Ⓓ The classmate is not correct. A line is a good representation of an arithmetic sequence.

21. Suppose ∠B and ∠C are the acute angles in ΔABC. If $\cos\angle B = \frac{7}{25}$, what is $\sin\angle C$?

   Ⓐ $\frac{7}{24}$

   Ⓑ $\frac{7}{25}$

   Ⓒ $\frac{24}{25}$

   Ⓓ $\frac{25}{7}$

22. The graph of a function given below shows a fluctuation in the winds created by an incoming storm over time. Over what intervals of time is the wind speed increasing?

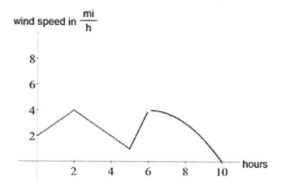

   Ⓐ [0, 2] only
   Ⓑ [2, 0] and [6, 5]
   Ⓒ [0, 2] and [5, 6]
   Ⓓ [2, 4] and [6, 10]

23. Which of the following graphs of a function has all of the following characteristics: Symmetry about the y-axis, has two relative maximums, and has five zeros.

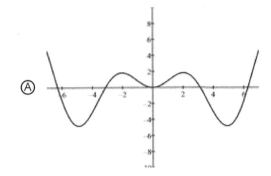
Ⓐ

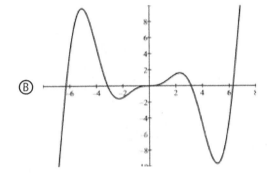
Ⓑ

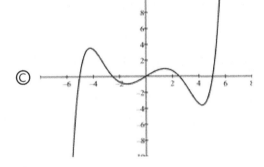
Ⓒ

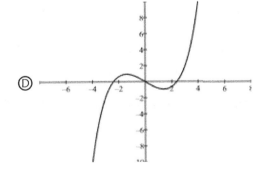
Ⓓ

24. The graph shown below shows an outbreak of the flu which has spread throughout a school for a period of 100 days. At day 40, there are 60 people that are infected with the flu. Which of the following statements best describes the relationship between the days and the number of people that have contracted the flu?

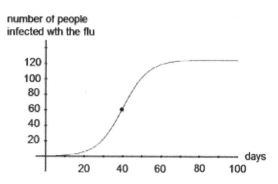

Ⓐ The number of people infected appears to be increasing at an increasing rate up to day 40 and then continues to increase but at a decreasing rate up to day 100.

Ⓑ The number of people that have contracted the flu appears to be increasing greatest at day 40.

Ⓒ The number of people that have contracted the flu appears to be decreasing at or around day 60.

Ⓓ After day 100 the number of people that have contracted the flu decreases to zero.

25. If you work at a job that pays you an hourly wage, your income each month is a function of the number of hours that you work each month. If S(a) is the function that is used for this situation then,

Ⓐ the domain of the function is S, the number of hours you work each month, and the range of the function is a, your monthly income.

Ⓑ the domain of the function is S, your monthly income, and the range of the function is a, the hourly wage you are paid to work each month.

Ⓒ the domain of the function is a, the number of hours you work each month, and the range of the function is S, your monthly income.

Ⓓ the domain of the function is a, your monthly income, and the range of the function is S, the number of hours you work each month.

26. An object that is thrown straight up at 30 ft./sec. at an initial height of 64 feet has a distance from the ground given by the function $h(t) = -16t^2 + 30t + 64$, where $h(t)$ represents the distance the object is from the ground, and t is time in seconds. What is the average rate of change for the function over the first second the object is thrown and what does the average rate of change mean in context of the problem?

Ⓐ -14 which is the average velocity of the object during the first second of time.
Ⓑ 14 which is the average velocity of the object during the first second of time.
Ⓒ -14, which means the object has fallen 14 feet after the first second of time.
Ⓓ 14, which means the object has risen 14 feet after the first second of time.

27. A survey of 9th and 10th graders was conducted to see which type of pet they preferred . The result of the survey is in the table.

What is the probability that a student prefers a cat, given that the student is a 10th grader?

Grade	Bird	Cat	Dog	Total
9	3	43	50	96
10	7	36	61	104
Total	10	79	111	200

Ⓐ $\frac{79}{200}$

Ⓑ $\frac{43}{96}$

Ⓒ $\frac{43}{200}$

Ⓓ $\frac{9}{26}$

28. Rewrite $\sqrt[4]{12a^3b^4c^5}$ using rational exponents.

Ⓐ $3a^{\frac{2}{4}}bc^{\frac{5}{4}}$
Ⓑ $12^{\frac{1}{4}}a^{\frac{3}{4}}bc^{\frac{5}{4}}$
Ⓒ $12^4a^{\frac{4}{3}}bc^{\frac{4}{5}}$
Ⓓ $12^4a^{12}b^{16}c^{20}$

29. During a collaborative activity, two students are discussing the population growth of caribou in Alaska displayed in this graph. They are tasked with making a conclusion about the population. Which choice is a likely conclusion they made?

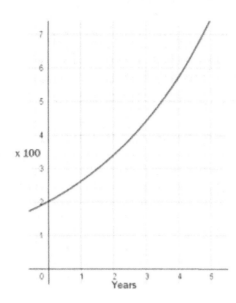

Ⓐ The population will increase until it reaches just over 700
Ⓑ The population will increase more in year 4 than it will increase in year 2
Ⓒ The population is declining
Ⓓ The population is increasing the same number every year

30. What is the first step in solving this equation?
    $4x - 7 = 21$

Ⓐ Add 7
Ⓑ Subtract 7
Ⓒ Multiply by 4
Ⓓ Divide by 4

31. What is the last step to solve the below equation for x ?

    $3\sqrt{x} + 4 = 13$

Ⓐ Square the equation
Ⓑ Subtract 4
Ⓒ Multiply by 3
Ⓓ Divide by 3

32. One afternoon, Lisa came home from the grocery store and told her husband that she bought 34 eggs for a women's breakfast she is planning. Her husband did not believe her. Based on his disbelief, how many eggs did he really think she bought?

33. The school nurse recorded the height in inches of a class. Below are the heights she recorded (in inches).

59, 60, 58, 55, 56, 57, 62, 57, 55, 54, 53, 50, 60, 57, 58, 64

She then constructs the following histogram. When double checking she notices she made an error. Where is the mistake?

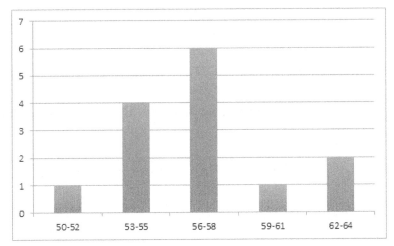

34. Match each term with the statement that best describes it.

	Box Plot	Histogram	Bar graph
Graph the number of strikes a pitcher makes in each of 12 games so that it is easy to see the median number of strikes achieved	O	O	O
Graph the color of cars a dealership sells. What color sells best?	O	O	O
Graph the scores on a quiz. Letter grades are given based on the score A = 90-100, B = 80-89 etc. Did more students score an A or a B?	O	O	O

35. Simply by looking at the two data sets below, which will have the greatest standard deviation. Explain why.

Set A -- 2,3,50,56,57,55,100,110
Set B -- 55,56,57,58,59,57,54,52,51

36. Match each statement with the graphical representation that will make it most easy to ``see'' the answer.

	Mean	Median	Standard Deviation	IQR
Measure distance from middle				
Measure of spread				
Is the middle number of a set arranged in numerical order				
Is the same as average				

Here are some reminders for when you are taking the Practice Test.

To answer the questions on the test, use the directions given in the question. If you do not know the answer to a question, skip it and go on to the next question. If time permits, you may return to questions in this session only. Do your best to answer every question.

Practice Test 2

1. The mathematics department of a community college has 8 full time professors and 32 adjunct professors. Each full time professor teaches 6 courses, and each adjunct professor teaches 2 courses. Each course requires an average of 1,350 sheets of paper for duplicating. If the department purchases paper in reams of 5000 sheets, how many reams of paper will the mathematics department purchase?

Ⓐ 31
Ⓑ 30
Ⓒ 29
Ⓓ 32

2. A survey of students in a class was conducted to record the color of hair each student has. The result of the survey is in the table. What is the probability that a girl has blonde hair?

Hair Color	Boys	Girls	Total
Brown	6	9	15
Black	3	5	8
Red	2	1	3
Blonde	4	6	10
Total	15	21	36

Ⓐ $\frac{2}{7}$

Ⓑ $\frac{7}{12}$

Ⓒ $\frac{3}{5}$

Ⓓ $\frac{4}{15}$

3. What is the coefficient of the first term in the expression $16x^2y^2-25$?

Ⓐ 16
Ⓑ 25
Ⓒ -25
Ⓓ 9

4. Use complete the squares to find the minimum value of : $f(x)=x^2+12x+3$. Circle the correct answer.

Ⓐ 6
Ⓑ -3
Ⓒ -33
Ⓓ -6

5. Which graph shows the solution of $y = \frac{1}{5}x^2 - \frac{4}{5}x - 1$?

Ⓐ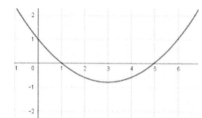

Ⓑ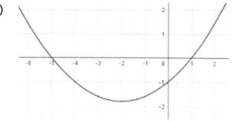

Ⓒ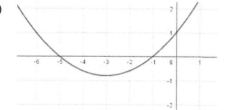

Ⓓ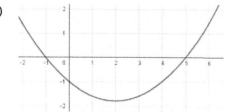

6. Dianna states that the sine of an acute angle is equal to the cosine of the complement of that same acute angle. Which choice proves Dianna's conjecture?

Ⓐ $\sin 45° = \dfrac{\sqrt{2}}{2}$, $\cos 45° = \dfrac{\sqrt{2}}{2}$

Ⓑ $\sin 60° = \dfrac{\sqrt{3}}{2}$, $\cos 30° = \dfrac{\sqrt{3}}{2}$

Ⓒ $\sin 75° = 0.9659$, $\cos 25° = 0.9659$

Ⓓ $\sin 65° = 0.9630$, $\cos 25° = 0.9630$

7. Your uncle is currently four times as old as you are. In five years, your uncle will be three times as old as you. What is your current age?

Ⓐ 10
Ⓑ 8
Ⓒ 5
Ⓓ 1

8. Alan can pull tree stumps from the ground at a rate of 4 tree stumps 1 hour. Steven can pull tree stumps from the ground at a rate of 9 tree stumps in 1½ hours. If they work together, how long will it take them to pull 40 tree stumps?

Ⓐ 13 hours
Ⓑ 7 hours
Ⓒ 5 ½ hours
Ⓓ 4 hours

9. You received a coupon in the mail for 10% off any meal at your favorite restaurant. You go to dinner that evening at the restaurant and order your meal that normally costs $15 before applying the coupon. The service and food was so good you decide to leave a tip of 20% of the discounted meal. Not including any taxes, what is the difference in what your total bill will be and the normal cost of the meal?

Ⓐ $16.50
Ⓑ $16.20
Ⓒ $1.50
Ⓓ $1.20

10. In science class, you conduct an experiment that involves recording the distance a rubber band car you have constructed travels along a straight line from a starting point after you have wound up the rubber band that propels the car down the hall way. You record the distance, measured in feet the car has traveled from the starting point over a 5 second interval of time. The recording is given below.

Time, t	1	2	3	4	5
Distance, d	8	11	14	17	20

According to the data collected, which of the following equations best represents the distance the car has traveled?

Ⓐ d=t+7

Ⓑ $d = \frac{1}{3}t + \frac{23}{3}$

Ⓒ d=3t+5

Ⓓ d=3t+1

11. Solve for x: 2x−4=3x−11.

Ⓐ x=15

Ⓑ x=7

Ⓒ x=-15

Ⓓ x=-7

12. Ms. Brunt asked her students to solve this equation 2x(2x−8)=0 for x. Ella wrote 4x²−16x=0 as her first step. What property did she use?

Ⓐ Distributive property

Ⓑ Associative property of multiplication

Ⓒ Identity property of addition

Ⓓ Commutative property of multiplication

13. What is the multiplicative inverse of $\frac{2}{3}$?

Ⓐ -1

Ⓑ $-\frac{3}{2}$

Ⓒ $-\frac{2}{3}$

Ⓓ $\frac{3}{2}$

14. If *a* and *b* are integers, which equation below will always be true?

Ⓐ $\left(\frac{a}{b}\right)\left(-\frac{a}{b}\right) = -1$

Ⓑ $a+3b=b+3a$

Ⓒ $a-1=b-1$

Ⓓ $ab=ba$

15. What is the solution to $9x+2=-52$?

Ⓐ 6

Ⓑ $-5.\overline{5}$

Ⓒ -6

Ⓓ $5.\overline{5}$

16. What is the solution to $2x-10=12$?

Ⓐ 11

Ⓑ 1

Ⓒ -1

Ⓓ -11

17. What is the solution to $3x-9=-48$?

Ⓐ 19

Ⓑ 13

Ⓒ -13

Ⓓ -19

18. The amount of money in an account is modeled by:
$$A=500(1+0.005)^{2t}$$
What is the rate of growth in the account on the interval $3 \le t \le 5$.
Answer with a percent. Explain your answer in detail.

19. Which statement is true about the domain and range of a function?

Ⓐ The domain is the set of outputs, the range is the set of inputs
Ⓑ The domain is the set of inputs, the range is the set of outputs
Ⓒ The range is the set of independent variables, the domain is the set of dependent
Ⓓ The domain is the set of independent variables, the range is the also the set of independent variables

20. Which function squares the input variable, then triples that value, adds five times the input variable and then subtracts twelve?

Ⓐ $f(x) = -3x^2 + 5x - 12$
Ⓑ $f(x) = 3x^2 + 5x - 12$
Ⓒ $f(x) = 3x^2 - 5x - 12$
Ⓓ $f(x) = 3x^2 + 5x + 12$

21. What is the recursive sequence for the arithmetic sequence shown below?
   9, 14, 19, 24

Ⓐ $a_n = a_{n-1} + 6$

Ⓑ $a_n = a_{n-1} * 5$

Ⓒ $a_n = a_{n-1} + 5$

Ⓓ $a_n = 14 + 5(n - 1)$

22. What is the recursive sequence for the arithmetic sequence shown below?
   −3, −15, −75, −375

Ⓐ $a_n = a_{n-1} * 3$

Ⓑ $a_n = a_1 * 3^{n-1}$

Ⓒ $a_n = a_{n-1} * 5$

Ⓓ $a_n = a_{n-1} * (-3)$

23. The line graph below shows the number of people at a festival from the time the gate opened until 12 hours later. What does the value 6 represent?

The x-axis shows "hours since opening" and the y-axis "number of people at the festival (hundreds)

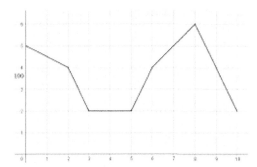

Ⓐ The maximum number of people at the festival was 600
Ⓑ The minimum number of people at the festival was 600
Ⓒ 600 people were at the festival when the gate opened
Ⓓ 600 people were at the festival when the gate closed

24. Given : $24 = 8e^{3t}$

Solve for "t" using logarithms. Express your answer to the nearest four decimal places. Show the working steps to arrive at the answer.

25. Chris conjectures that if he takes the promotion that has been offered to him, he should be able to save more than enough money in 6 months to buy a new laptop computer he has been wanting. His new salary will be $10.50 per hour plus a $300 bonus for taking the offer. Chris is limited to working 40 hours each month because of school. If the laptop computer costs $400 and Chris has a car payment of $300 per month and has to spend $100 per month on gas, will he make more than enough money to buy the laptop computer? Use a mathematical argument to support your answer.

26. You cook a pie in the oven at 450 degrees. After taking the cooked pie out of the oven in a kitchen that is 70 degrees, you need to allow it to cool(so you won't burn your tongue) before you can eat it. The graph of the temperature of the pie as well as a few points on the graph of the temperatures at certain times, t , in minutes is shown below. Estimate the average rate of change in the temperature of the pie during the first 10 minutes and describe what it means in context of the temperature of the pie.

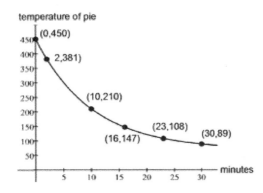

Ⓐ The average rate of change is -24. In context to the problem, it means the temperature is decreasing at 24 degrees per minute.

Ⓑ The average rate of change is 24. In context to the problem, it means the temperature is increasing at 24 degrees per minute.

Ⓒ The average rate of change is -10. In context to the problem, it means the temperature has dropped 10 degrees in 10 minutes.

Ⓓ The average rate of change is -24. In context to the problem, it means the temperature has dropped 24 degrees in the first 10 minutes.

27. The number of homework problems you can complete is given by the function $h(t) = \frac{2}{5}t + 6$, where t represents time in minutes. You want to know how many homework assignments you can finish in a given period of time and find that you can finish $A(h) = \frac{h}{15} + 1$ number of assignments, where A represents a homework assignment that you have finished. Find $(A \circ h)(60)$ and tell what that value means.

Ⓐ 3, which is the number of problems you can finish in 60 minutes.
Ⓑ 3, which is the number of assignments you can finish in 60 minutes.
Ⓒ 1, which is the number of assignments you can finish in 60 minutes.
Ⓓ 8, which is the number of assignments you can finish in 60 minutes.

28. The function $f(x) = -\frac{1}{3}(x - 6)^2$ is the path of a fly ball at a major league baseball game. Its graph is shown below. What is the domain of this function? Circle the correct answer.

Time (seconds)

Ⓐ [6,0]
Ⓑ [-1,7]
Ⓒ $(-\infty, \infty)$
Ⓓ [0,6]

29. Suppose the cost of electricity in Florida is 11.6 cents per kilowatt hour (kWh) , and the cost of electricity in Georgia is 10.1 cents per kilowatt hour. What is the difference between electricity costs in Florida and in Georgia if a customer consumes 2,124kWh?

Ⓐ $246.38
Ⓑ $31.86
Ⓒ $214.52
Ⓓ $460.90

30. When solving an exponential equation, we must convert the exponential equation to a logarithmic equation. Which process correctly converts the exponential equation $26=4(3)^{2x}$ to a logarithmic equation?

Ⓐ $\log 26 = 2x\log[4(3)]$

Ⓑ $\log \frac{26}{4} = 2x\log3$

Ⓒ $26 = 8x\log3$

Ⓓ $\log 26 = 4x\log3^2$

31. Maria and Gorvick are comparing investment options for their vacation account. They see one option that compounds the interest annually. Based on their initial investment of $1000, they anticipate an account balance shown in the table below.

Year	Balance
3	$ 1,061.21
5	$ 1,104.08

A friend of theirs tells them they could earn more interest if the interest was compounded more often, even if the interest rate is the same. Which option compounds the most often?

Ⓐ $A = 1000\left(1 + \frac{0.05}{12}\right)^{12t}$

Ⓑ $A = 1000\left(1 + \frac{0.05}{2}\right)^{2t}$

Ⓒ $A = 1000\left(1 + \frac{0.05}{52}\right)^{52t}$

Ⓓ $A = 1000\left(1 + \frac{0.05}{4}\right)^{4t}$

32. Suppose ΔABC ~ ΔDEF shown below. What is tan E ?

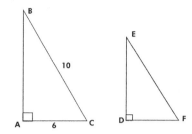

Ⓐ $\frac{3}{5}$

Ⓑ $\frac{4}{3}$

Ⓒ $\frac{3}{4}$

Ⓓ $\frac{4}{5}$

33. Sin ∠S= $\frac{5}{3}$ in ΔRST as shown below. What is the length of $\overline{RS}$?

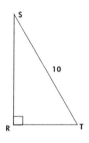

Ⓐ 8

Ⓑ 7

Ⓒ 6

Ⓓ 9

34. Given the data below what is the median test scores for Ms. Anderson's class?

Test Grades for Ms. Anderson

Ⓐ 70
Ⓑ 75
Ⓒ 80
Ⓓ 85

35. Below are test scores from Ms. Johnson's class and Mr. Smith's class. Which class has the highest median score and by how many points?

Test Grades for Ms. Johnson   Test Grades for Ms. Smith

Ⓐ Ms. Johnson's class has the highest median score by 20 points.
Ⓑ Mr. Smith's class has the highest median score by 20 points.
Ⓒ Ms. Johnson's class has the highest median score by 10 points.
Ⓓ Mr. Smith's class has the highest median score by 10 points.

36. Match each statement with the graphical representation that will make it most easy to "see" the answer. Fill the circles that applies.

	Mean	Median	Standard Deviation	IQR
Measure distance from middle	○	○	○	○
Measure of spread	○	○	○	○
Is the middle number of a set arranged in numerical order	○	○	○	○
Is the same as average	○	○	○	○

Practice Test 1

Answer Key & Detailed Explanations

Question No.	Answer	Detailed Explanation
1	A	The question asks for an exponential model, which is the formula $y=ab^x$. Use formula and the points in the table to solve for a, for both lines in the table: $$160 = ab^5; a = \frac{160}{b^5}; 640 = ab^7; a = \frac{640}{b^7}.$$ Make the two expression equal to each other in a proportion and solve for b by cross multiplying: $$\frac{160}{b^5} = \frac{640}{b^7}; 160b^7 = 640b^5; b^2 = 4; b = 2.$$ Last, use the value of b in the formula to solve for a: $y = ab^x$; $160 = a(2)^5$; $160 = 32a$; $a = 5$. The model is $y = 5(2)^x$.
2	C	According to the y intercept of the graph, the share price was $2 when Jack purchased the shares. He wants to sell the shares when their price is $4. Each number on the x-axix represents a month, and the first month is the interval [0 ,1]. Notice that the share price is $4 at approximately 7.2 on the s-axis. This is in the interval [7, 8], which is during the 8th month.
3	C	When we raise a number to an even power, the sign of the result is always positive because a number to a positive exponent is positive. However, when we take a root of a number, unless we are asked to find all possible roots, we only find the primary root which is always positive. Therefore, in the formula, $\sqrt[a]{n^a} = n$ for any even number a, is true only if n is positive. Thus, to find the primary root of $\sqrt[4]{(-7)^4}$,we need a positive answer, making an absolute value symbol necessary when dealing with variables.
4	E	Find the zeros of a quadratic expression by factoring the expression and then setting each factor equal to zero. $6x^2 - 17x - 14 = (3x + 2)(2x - 7)$; $3x + 2 = 0$ if $x = -\frac{2}{3}$ and $2x - 7 = 0$ if $x = \frac{7}{2}$.
5		They would be the same. y_1 and y_2 are the same equation, y_1 is a quadratic in factored form.

Question No.	Answer	Detailed Explanation
6	D	Even integers are 2 numbers apart. If we select the variable x as the smallest of the three numbers, the variable expressions for the three numbers are x, $x+2$, and $x+4$. Write an equation that shows the sum of these three expressions is 72 and solve the equation. $x+x+2+x+4=72$ $3x+6=72$ $2x=66$ $x=22$ We want the middle numbers, so we use $x+2=24$
7	A	The formula for the perimeter of a rectangle is $P=2l+2w$. Solve this formula using the information given: $300=2(2w)+2w$, $w=50$; $l=100$. The area of a rectangle is: $A=lw=100\times50=5000$
8	B	The variable x represents the number of hours after the store opens, so the minimum value of x is 0. Based on the given equation, the last case of water is sold 9 hours after the store opens. Thus, the domain is [0,9].
9	C	To solve for b, multiply both sides by 2, divided by h, and subtract B. $A = \frac{1}{2}h(B + b); 2A = h(B + b); \frac{2A}{h} = B + b; b = \frac{2A}{h} - B$
10	B & D	The difference in w(t) and p(t) yields answer B. $w(t)-p(t)=(t^3-t^2+100)-(t^3-3t^2+300)$ $=t^3-t^2+100-t^3+3t^2-300$ $=2t^2-200$. Factoring $2t^2-200$ we get answer D. $2t^2-200=2(t^2-100)=2(t-10)(t+10)$.
11	C	Solving an inequality is done the same way as solving an equation, except, if you multiply or divide by a negative number, the direction of the inequality symbol changes. Solve the given inequality by subtracting 7 and dividing by 5. The direction of the inequality symbol does not change. $5x+7\geq32$; $5x\geq25$; $x\geq5$

LumosLearning.com

Question No.	Answer	Detailed Explanation
12	C	To solve an equation for a variable, the goal is to get the variable by itself. The steps for solving an equation are: (1) if there are parenthesis, distribute to remove them, (2) combine like terms, (3) move terms with the variable to one side, (4) move terms without the variable to the other side, and (5) multiply or divide by the co-efficient of the variable. In the given equation, distribute the 4. Then, combine $-20+5$ now, and add the result to both sides. Last, divide by 4. $4(x-5)+5=21$; $4x-20+5=21$; $4x-15=21$; $4x=36$; $x=9$
13	A	In mathematics, the graph of a function f(x) is the collection of all ordered pairs (x,f(x)) that are solutions to a function. The given line can be written as a function: $$f(x) = \frac{1}{3}x + 2$$
14	A	Change the equation so it equals zero. Then, factor the quadratic trinomial, set each factor equal to zero, and solve for the variable in each factor. $y=x^2-2x-8$; $0=x^2-2x-8$; $0=(x+2)(x-4)$; $x=-2, x=4$
15	B	A function is written as: $f(x)=y$ where x is put into the function f. This is why the variable x is called the input variable. The result of putting x into the function is y. This is why the variable y is called the output variable. Furthermore, the value of y depends on the value of x.
16	B & C	If we solve the quadratic inequality for x, we can eliminate the time it would take to guess and check for answers. Now $-x^2-2x<-8$, $-x^2-2x+8<0$, $x^2+2x-8>0$. Set the inequality equal to zero we can find the zeros, then we can test values for x which make the inequality greater than zero. $x^2+2x-8=0$, $(x+4)(x-2)=0$, $x=-4$ or $x=2$. Test values will confirm the inequality is less than -8 when $x<-4$ or $x>2$ $x=-5$ we have $-(-5)^2-2(-5)=-25+10=-14<-8$ and $x=3$ we have $-(3)^2-2(3)=-9-6=-15<-8$.

Question No.	Answer	Detailed Explanation
17		Student must follow the equation line by line and then identify that ``Catherine'' did not apply the distributive property correctly; she failed to multiply 5 and 1, causing the answer to be incorrect.
18	A	Find f(x) + g(x) by combining like terms. $h(x) = (x^2 - 3x + 9) + (6x^2 - 4x - 7)$ $h(x) = (x^2 + 6x^2) + (-3x + -4x) + (9 + -7)$ $h(x) = 7x^2 - 7x + 2$
19	D	If two triangles are similar, all of their corresponding sides form the same ratios. The cosine function is the ratio of the adjacent side to the hypotenuse. $\triangle ABC$ and $\triangle DEF$, $\angle C$ and $\angle F$ corresponding angles, so their adjacent sides and hypotenuse also correspond. The cosine of $\angle C$ is the same as the cosine of $\angle F$.
20	C	A sequence can be defined as a function whose domain consists of the set of consecutive positive integers. Therefore, a line is not a good representation of any sequence for several reasons. First, the domain of all non-vertical lines is the set of all real numbers, whereas the domain of any sequence is the set of all positive integers (remember, zero is neither positive nor negative). Second, a sequence is a set of discrete numbers, whose values are not continuous. A line contains a continuous set of numbers.
21	B	The cosine function of an angle is the ratio of the length of the adjacent side to the length of the hypotenuse. The sine function of an angle is the ratio of the length of the opposite side to the length of the hypotenuse. In a right triangle, the opposite side of one acute angle is the adjacent side of the other acute angle. Therefore, the cosine of one acute angle is the sine of the other acute angle.
22	C	The correct answer is C. The wind speed is increasing whenever the graph of the function is moving upwards from left to right, that is the slope is positive. Also note there is a hole in the graph at the point (6,4), thus we cannot include (6,4) as a point on our interval which is why answer B is incorrect.

Question No.	Answer	Detailed Explanation
23	A	The correct answer is A. Reflecting the graph of answer A about the y-axis produces an equivalent graph, therefore graph of A is symmetric about the y-axis. Since the graph of answer A is the only graph that has y-axis symmetry the answer must default to A. Note: Answers B, C, D all have symmetry about the origin.
24	A & B	The correct answers are A and B. This type of curve is called a logistics curve. It is a type of an exponential curve, however there is some point on the graph where the curve begins to change in how it increases or decreases. This point is called a point of inflection. For this particular situation, the point of inflection is at (40,60). Notice that the graph of the curve is still increasing after day 40, but not as fast as it is before day 40. Answer D might be true and we certainly hope it will be, but we don't have any information after day 100 so we cannot make that conjecture.
25	C	The correct answer is C. In function notation, S(a) is telling us that S is dependent on what a is. Since your monthly income is clearly dependent on how many hours you work in a month, a is the independent variable, which is how we define the domain of a function. Thus S is the range.
26	B	To find the average rate of change we are actually find the slope of the line between two points given as, $m = \frac{y_2 - y_1}{x_2 - x_1}$, where m is the slope and (x_1,y_1), (x_2,y_2) are two points on the line. So the average rate of change from 0 to 1 second is, $\frac{h(1) - h(0)}{1 - 0} = \frac{[-16(1)^2 + 30(1) + 64] - [-16(0)^2 + 30(0) + 64]}{1} = 14$. This rate of change is the average velocity since we are determining the rate of change in the object's position in a given period of time.
27	D	The two-way table shows how many students, by grade, prefer each pet. If we are given that the student is a 10th grader, we need to only look at the 10th grade row. We can see that 36 out of 104 10th graders prefer a cat. This ratio reduces to $\frac{9}{26}$.

Question No.	Answer	Detailed Explanation
28	B	To convert a radical expression, such as $\sqrt[4]{12a^3b^4c^5}$ consider that the index of the radical can be written as a rational exponent of the radical (the expression inside the radical). $\sqrt[4]{12a^3b^4c^5} = (12a^3b^4c^5)^{\frac{1}{4}}$ Then, use the power of a power rule for exponents and multiply the exponents inside the parenthesis by the exponent outside the parenthesis: $(12a^3b^4c^5)^{\frac{1}{4}} = 12^{1(\frac{1}{4})}a^{3(\frac{1}{4})}b^{4(\frac{1}{4})}c^{5(\frac{1}{4})} = 12^{\frac{1}{4}}a^{\frac{3}{4}}bc^{\frac{5}{4}}$
29	B	The increase in year 2 is 340-260=80. The increase in year 4 is 560-440=120.
30	A	To solve an equation for a variable, the goal is to get the variable by itself. The steps for solving an equation are: (1) if there are parenthesis, distribute to remove them, (2) combine like terms, (3) move terms with the variable to one side, (4) move terms without the variable to the other side, and (5) multiply or divide by the coefficient of the variable. The given equation does not have any parenthesis, so begin by moving 7 to the side that does not contain the variable. Move positive numbers by subtracting them, and move negative numbers by adding them.
31	A	To solve the equation, isolate the radical and then square the equation. Begin by subtracting 4 from both sides. Next, divide both sides by 3. Square the equation. $3\sqrt{x}+4=13$; $3\sqrt{x}=9$; $\sqrt{x}=3$ Hence, x=9.
32		Correct Answer : 36 Her husband assumes that his wife buys eggs by the dozen. A dozen is 12. The quantity 34 is not a multiple of 12 . Lisa's husband assumes she bought 3 dozen eggs.
33		For the values between 59-61 there are 3 scores: 59, 60, and 60. The bar extending in the 59-61 column should go to 3.
34		#1 -- The box plot best shows the median in a set of data. #2 -- Graphing different classifications such as color, shape, type and in an effort to determine highest or lowest values is accomplished most easily with a bar graph. #3 -- Histograms work best for determining quantities present in a range.

Question No.	Answer	Detailed Explanation
35		Data Set A will have a greater standard deviation. Notice that the middle values of both data sets are in the 50's. In fact all the data points in Set B are in the 50's. However, Set A has points as low as 2 and as high as 110. These values that are far away from the middle result in a higher standard deviation.
36		#1 -- The mean and median help determine how close to the middle data is.

#2 -- The way data is spread out is part of standard deviation and IQR.

#3 -- The median is the number that falls in the middle when the data is arranged in numerical order.

#4 -- The mean is the same as the average. |

Practice Test 2

Answer Key & Detailed Explanations

Question No.	Answer	Detailed Explanation
1	A	The full time professors teach 48 classes and the adjunct professors teach 64 classes, totaling 112 classes. At 1,350 sheets per class, this gives a requirement of 151,200 sheets. Dividing the number of sheets by 5000 gives 30.24 The department must purchase 31 reams.
2	A	The two-way table shows how many students, by boys or girls, have each hair color. If we are given that the student is a girl, we need to only look at the column for girls. We can see that 6 out of 21 girls have blonde. This ratio reduces to $\frac{2}{7}$.
3	A	The expression $16x^2y^2-25$ is a binomial expression, meaning it has two terms. The coefficient of a term is the number in the front of the term, whether or not the term has variables. The first term is $16x^2y^2$ and the number in the front of the term is 16.
4	C	Complete the squares by identifying the correct value of c in the expression $x^2+12x+c$ to create an expression that includes a square of a binomial. To find c, we follow these steps: $f(x)=x^2+12x+3$ $=x^2+12x+c+3-c$ $=x^2+12x+36+3-36$ $=(x^2+12x+36)-33$ $=(x+6)^2-33$ The given function is a parabola that opens upward. The y value in the vertex is the minimum value of the function. The final expression above is the vertex form of the function, with a vertex of (-6, -33).
5	D	Change the equation $y=\frac{1}{5}x^2-\frac{4}{5}x-1$ to $0=\frac{1}{5}x^2-\frac{4}{5}x-1$. Next, factor the equation: $0=(x+1)\left(\frac{1}{5}x-1\right)$ Set each factor equal to zero, and the solution has x-intercepts of -1 and 5.

Question No.	Answer	Detailed Explanation
6	A & B	$\sin 45° = \dfrac{\sqrt{2}}{2}$, $\cos 45° = \dfrac{\sqrt{2}}{2}$ correctly states the conjecture. In the choice: $\sin 60° = \dfrac{\sqrt{3}}{2}$, $\cos 30° = \dfrac{\sqrt{3}}{2}$, the two angles are complementary, and correctly states the conjecture. In the choice: $\sin 75° = 0.9659$, $\cos 25° = 0.9659$, the two angles are not complementary. In the choice: $\sin 65° = 0.9630$, $\cos 25° = 0.9630$, the correct value for the two trigonometric functions is: 0.9063.
7	A	The correct answer is A. Let your current age be n then your uncle's current age is 4n. In 5 years, your age will be n + 5. Your uncle's age will be 4n + 5. Since your uncle is three times older than you in five years we can set up the equivalence statement, $4n + 5 = 3(n + 5)$ $4n + 5 = 3n + 15$ $n = 10$. Thus, your current age is 10 years old.
8	D	The correct answer is D. Alan can pull stumps at a rate of 4 per hour, so he will pull 4t stumps in t hours. Steven pulls the stumps at a rate of 9 per 1½ hours or $$\dfrac{9}{1\frac{1}{2}} = \dfrac{9}{\frac{3}{2}} = 9 * \dfrac{2}{3} = 6 = 6$$ per hour. Thus Steven pulls 6t stumps in t hours. If they work together, they will pull 4t+6t stumps in t hours. To find the time t it will take to pull 40 tree stumps set 4t + 6t = 40 and solve for t to get t = 4.
9	D	The correct answer is D. The cost of your discount meal is $15 minus 10% of $15 or, $15 - 0.10(15) = \$13.50$. Your tip is applied to $13.50, so the total bill is, $13.50 + 0.20(13.50) = 13.50 + 2.70 = \$16.20$. Finally, the difference between your total bill and the normal cost of the bill is $\$16.20 - \$15.00 = \$1.20$.

Question No.	Answer	Detailed Explanation
10	C	Since the car moving along a straight line we can write a linear equation using the slope-intercept for y=mx+b. We will adjust the domain and range and use d=mt+b for our problem. Now, using the first 2 data points (1,8) and (2,11) we have, $$m = \frac{d_2 - d_1}{t_2 - t_1} = \frac{11 - 8}{2 - 1} = 3.$$ Next, to find *b* we substitute the calculated slope and one of the data points into d=mt+b to get, 8=3(1)+b, 8=3+b, 5=b. Substituting m and b into d=mt+b we get d=3t+5. Thus the correct answer is C.
11	B	Student must solve this equation with variables on both sides for *x* by applying inverse operations and grouping like terms on either side of the equal sign; alternatively a student might test each of the answer choices in the equation using substitution and find which one balances the equation.
12	A	She distributed the 2x to the binomial expression 2x−8.
13	D	Student must demonstrate knowledge of the multiplicative inverse which is the reciprocal of any real number; student must understand that the product of a number and its multiplicative inverse is one; this is commonly used in solving equations that involve fractions.
14	D	The only answer choice that holds true is d because of the commutative property of multiplication; the other equations are only true if a=b.
15	C	The question asks you to find the solution to 9x+2=-52. Begin by subtracting 2 from both sides of the equation. This gives you 9x=-54. Next, divide both sides by 9 and x=-6.
16	A	The question asks you to find the solution to 2x-10=12. Begin by adding 10 to both sides of the equation. This gives you 2x=22. Next, divide both sides by 2 and x=11.
17	C	The question asks you to find the solution to 3x-9=-48. Begin by adding 9 to both sides of the equation. This gives you 3x=-39. Next, divide both sides by 3 and x=-13.

Question No.	Answer	Detailed Explanation
18		Calculate the amount in the account when t=3 and t=5. Then divide A(5) by A(3). $A(3)=500(1+0.005)^{2*3} = 515.1887547$ $A(5)=500(1+0.005)^{2*5} = 525.570066$ $$\frac{A(5)}{A(3)} = \frac{525.570066}{515.1888547} = 1.02$$ The amount in the account grew 2 percent.
19	B	A function is written as: f(x)=y where x is put into the function f. This is why the variable x is called the input variable. The result of putting x into the function is y. This is why the variable y is called the output variable. Furthermore, the value of y depends on the value of x.
20	B	The input variable is x. Squaring the input variable is a term x^2. Tripling that value is a term $3x^2$. Adding five times the input variable is the term +5x. Subtracting twelve is the term -12. Put together, we have $f(X)=3x^2+5x-12$.
21	C	A recursive formula uses the previous term to find the next term. In an arithmetic sequence, the recursive formula is: $a_n = a_{n-1} + d$ where n is the term number and d is the common difference between each term. The given sequence is an arithmetic sequence, where each term is 5 more than the previous term, so the common difference is 5 Therefore, to find the next term, add 5 to the previous term, giving a formula of : $a_n = a_{n-1} + 5$
22	C	A recursive formula uses the previous term to find the next term. In a geometric sequence, the recursive formula is $a_n = a_{n-1}*r$, where the nth term is number and r is the common ratio between each term. The given sequence is a geometric sequence, where each term is 5 times the previous term, so the common ratio is 5. Therefore, to find the next term, multiply the previous term by 5, giving a formula of $a_n = a_{n-1}*r$
23	A	The scale of the graph for the dependent variable shows x 100 Thus, the number 6 represents 600 people. If you look at the graph, you can see that the highest point on the graph is where the value is 6 , so the 6 represents the maximum number of people at the festival.

Question No.	Answer	Detailed Explanation
24		Correct Answer : 0.3662 Solve for t by dividing by 8 taking the natural logarithm of both sides using the exponent rules, recognize that ln e = 1, and dividing both sides by 3 to isolate t. Last, round as required. $24 = 8e^{3t}$; $3 = e^{3t}$; $\ln 3 = 3t \ln e$; $t = \dfrac{\ln 3}{3} = 0.3662040962$
25		Chris's new salary s can be written as s(t)=10.50t +300. If he works the maximum of 40 hours each month then in 6 months his salary will be s(240) = 10.50(240)+300= \$2,820. He has to spend 300 x 6 + 100 x 6 = \$2,400 on his car and gas for the 6 month period. To buy the computer he must make at least \$2,800, so he will have to work more than 238 hours since s(238)=10.50(238)+300=\$2,799. So Chris will have to work either 239 hours or 240 hours in order to buy the new laptop.
26	A	The correct answer is A. The question is asking you to approximate the slope of the line thru the points (0,450) and (10,210). Doing so we use, $m = \dfrac{y_2 - y_1}{x_2 - x_1}$, where m is the slope and (x_1, y_1), (x_2, y_2) are two points on the line. Now, $m = \dfrac{y_2 - y_1}{x_2 - x_1}$, $m = \dfrac{210 - 450}{10 - 0} = -24$. In context of the problem, the slope represents the rate of change in degrees over the change in time or the change in degrees per minute. Since this rate is negative, the temperature is decreasing at 24 degrees per minute.
27	B	The correct answer is B. The number of assignments finished is dependent on the number of homework problems you can finish in t minutes. So we must first find how many problems we can finish in a given time in order to determine how many assignments we can complete. First, evaluate h(60). Its' value becomes the domain for A(h). We get, $(A \circ h)(60) = A(h(60)) = A(\frac{2}{5} * 60 + 6) = A(30) = \frac{30}{15} + 1 = 3$. Note: Answer A would be correct, however it explains the answer as the number of problems solved.

Question No.	Answer	Detailed Explanation
28	D	The function is a polynomial function. The domain of a all polynomial functions, in a mathematical context is $(-\infty, \infty)$. However, in a real world context, the domain must allow the function to obey the rules of the real world. The ball is hit at time equals 0 seconds, and the ball lands, according to the graph, at time equals 6 seconds. Therefore, the domain is [0, 6].
29	B	Calculate the electricity costs in each state by multiplying the consumption by the unit price. Then, subtract one cost from the other. Florida: 2,124 * $0.116 = $246.38 Georgia: 2,124 * $0.101 = $214.52 $246.38 - $214.52 = $31.86
30	B	To convert an exponential equation to a logarithmic equation, isolate the part of the equation that is raised to a power. Then, take the logarithm of each side. The purpose of taking the logarithm is to use the exponent rule of logarithms to move the variable expression from the exponent out of the exponent. The steps to get the equation $\log \frac{26}{4} = 2x\log 3$ were: divide both sides by 4 exponential expression, and take the logarithm of both sides, using the exponent rule of logarithms to move the exponent (2x) out of the exponent. Now, we could solve for x using division.
31	C	The choices are all compound interest equations, using the formula: $A = 1000\left(1 + \frac{r}{n}\right)^{nt}$, where n is the number of times interest is compounded per year. Review the choices, one choice compounds semi-annually(2 times per year), another choice compounds quarterly(4 times per year), a third choice compounds monthly(12 times per year). The best choice compounds weekly(52 times per year). This means that every week, the interest that is earned is added to the account balance so it, too, can earn interest.
32	C	Use the Pythagorean Theorem, or you knowledge of Pythagorean triples to find the length of the missing side. If two triangles are similar, all of their corresponding sides form the same ratios. The tangent function is the ratio of the opposite side to the adjacent side .In $\triangle ABC$ and $\triangle DEF$, $\angle B$ and $\angle E$ are corresponding angles, so their opposite sides and adjacent sides also correspond. The tangent of $\angle B$ is the same as the tangent of $\angle E$.

Question No.	Answer	Detailed Explanation
33	A	In $\triangle RST$, the length of the hypotenuse is 10. Since $\sin \angle S = \frac{3}{5}$, and sine is the ratio of the length of the opposite side to the length of the hypotenuse, the ratio of $\overline{RT}$ to $\overline{ST}$ is $\frac{3}{5}$. Write and solve a proportion: $\frac{3}{5} = \frac{\overline{RT}}{10}$; $5 * \overline{RT} = 30$; $\overline{RT} = 6$. Now that we know the lengths of the hypotenuse and one of the legs, we can use the Pythagorean Theorem to find the length of the other leg $\overline{RS}$. $a^2 + b^2 = c^2$; $6^2 + b^2 = 10^2$; $36 + b^2 = 100$; $b^2 = 64$; $b = 8$; $b = \overline{RS} = 8$.
34	C	Begin by placing the scores in order. 50, 50, 50, 60, 60, 70, 70, 70, 70, 80, 80, 80, 90, 90, 90, 90, 90, 100, 100, 100, 100, 100, 100 There are 23 scores. The middle number is an 80. Notice below that there are 11 scores before and after the 80. 50, 50, 50, 60, 60, 70, 70, 70, 70, 80, 80, <u>80</u>, 90, 90, 90, 90, 90, 100, 100, 100, 100, 100, 100
35	D	Begin by placing the scores in order for Ms. Johnson's class. 50, 50, 50, 60, 60, 70, 70, 70, 70, 70, 80, 80, 80, 90, 90, 90, 90, 90, 100, 100, 100, 100, 100, 100, 100 There are 25 scores. The middle number is an 80. Notice below that there are 12 scores before and after the 80. 50, 50, 50, 60, 60, 70, 70, 70, 70, 70, 80, 80, 80, 90, 90, 90, 90, 90, 100, 100, 100, 100, 100, 100, 100 Now place the scores in order for Mr. Smith's class. 60, 70, 70, 70, 70, 70, 80, 80, 90, 90, 90, 90, 90, 90, 90, 100, 100, 100, 100, 100, 100 There are 21 scores. The middle number is an 90. Notice below that there are 10 scores before and after the 90. 60, 70, 70, 70, 70, 70, 80, 80, 90, 90, 90, 90, 90, 90, 90, 100, 100, 100, 100, 100, 100

Question No.	Answer	Detailed Explanation
36		#1 -- The mean and median help determine how close to the middle data is.
		#2 -- The way data is spread out is part of standard deviation and IQR.
		#3 -- The median is the number that falls in the middle when the data is arranged in numerical order.
		#4 -- The mean is the same as the average.

Chapter 1 - Real Numbers

1. Evaluate $49^{\frac{3}{2}}$

- Ⓐ 7
- Ⓑ 147
- Ⓒ 21
- Ⓓ 343

2. Evaluate $9^{\frac{150}{300}}$

- Ⓐ 18
- Ⓑ 9
- Ⓒ 3
- Ⓓ 81

3. Which of the following expressions is an equivalent simplified radical exponent expression for $9^{\frac{2}{5}}$ **?**

- Ⓐ 3^5
- Ⓑ $\sqrt{9^5}$
- Ⓒ $(\sqrt[5]{9})^2$
- Ⓓ $(\sqrt{9})^5$

4. Which of the following expressions is an equivalent simplified expression for $(125^{\frac{3}{2}})^{\frac{4}{9}}$ **?**

- Ⓐ $5^{\frac{2}{3}}$
- Ⓑ 25
- Ⓒ $125^{\frac{3}{2}}$
- Ⓓ 5

5. Which of the following expressions is an equivalent simplified radical exponent expression for $(6^{\frac{1}{7}})^{\frac{7}{2}}$ **?**

- Ⓐ 6
- Ⓑ 36
- Ⓒ $\sqrt{36}$
- Ⓓ $\sqrt{6}$

6. Rewrite the radical expression $\sqrt[4]{x^3}$ as an expression with rational exponents, using the properties of exponents.

Ⓐ $x^{\frac{4}{3}}$
Ⓑ $x^{\frac{3}{4}}$
Ⓒ $x^{\frac{1}{4}}$
Ⓓ $x^{\frac{1}{12}}$

7. Rewrite the radical expression $\sqrt[7]{x^5y^6}$ as an expression with rational exponents, using the properties of exponents.

Ⓐ $x^{\frac{7}{5}}y^{\frac{7}{6}}$
Ⓑ $(x^5y^6)^7$
Ⓒ $(x^{\frac{1}{5}}y^{\frac{1}{6}})^7$
Ⓓ $x^{\frac{5}{7}}y^{\frac{6}{7}}$

8. Rewrite the radical expression $\sqrt[4]{(abc)^9}$ as an expression with rational exponents, using the properties of exponents.

Ⓐ $(abc)^{\frac{9}{4}}$
Ⓑ $(abc)^{\frac{4}{9}}$
Ⓒ $(abc)^{36}$
Ⓓ $(abc)^5$

9. Rewrite $x^{\frac{1}{2}}$ in radical form.

Ⓐ $\sqrt{x}$
Ⓑ $\sqrt{x^2}$
Ⓒ $\frac{1}{\sqrt{x}}$
Ⓓ $-\sqrt{x}$

10. Which of the following is equal to 100?

Ⓐ $\sqrt[3]{1000}$
Ⓑ $100^{\frac{3}{2}}$
Ⓒ $1000^{\frac{2}{3}}$
Ⓓ $\sqrt{1000}$

11. Add $0.\overline{201}$ and $\frac{2}{9}$. What type of number is the result?

Ⓐ The numbers cannot be added
Ⓑ 0.401, rational
Ⓒ 0.423 irrational
Ⓓ $\frac{47}{111}$, rational

12. Multiply $\sqrt[4]{729}$ and $\frac{5}{7}$. What type of number is the result?

Ⓐ The numbers cannot be multiplied

Ⓑ $\frac{5\sqrt[4]{729}}{7}$, rational

Ⓒ 3.712, rational

Ⓓ $\frac{5\sqrt[4]{729}}{7}$, irrational

13. Multiply 3.12112111211112... and 3. What type of number is the result?

Ⓐ The numbers cannot be multiplied
Ⓑ 9.36336333633336..., rational
Ⓒ 3.712, rational
Ⓓ 9.36336333633336..., irrational

14. Add 2.123123412345123456...and $\frac{25}{64}$. Which of the following is an approximation of the answer?

Ⓐ The numbers cannot be added
Ⓑ 2.513625, rational
Ⓒ 2.513irrational
Ⓓ 2.5137..., irrational

15. Simplify $5\sqrt{3} - \sqrt{3}$.

Ⓐ $5\sqrt{3}$
Ⓑ $4\sqrt{3}$
Ⓒ 5
Ⓓ 4

Chapter 2 - Quantities

1. The graph below represents the approximate drag on an aircraft while in flight in that the drag on the aircraft is equal to a coefficient times the cube of the velocity. Which statement is true about the origin on the graph?

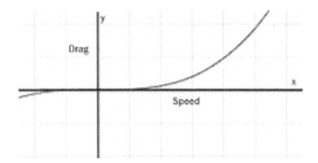

Ⓐ The origin shows the amount of drag after the airplane is in the air.
Ⓑ The origin shows that when the aircraft is not flying there is no drag.
Ⓒ The origin shows that the drag is increasing.
Ⓓ The origin shows that the drag changes from negative to positive.

2. The graph below shows the driving speed of a car over an 8 hour period in a mileage test. The speed limit on the freeway is universally 70 miles per hour, except when passing through cities, when the speed limit is reduced. The driver of the car obeyed all speed limits during the test. Which statement is true about the units on the y-axis of the graph?

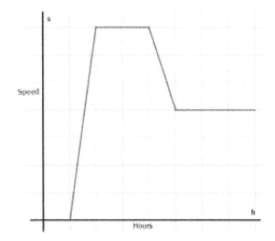

Ⓐ Each mark on the axis is approximately 10 miles per hour.
Ⓑ Each mark on the axis is approximately 7 miles.
Ⓒ Each mark on the axis is approximately 12 miles per hour.
Ⓓ Each mark on the axis is approximately 9 miles.

3. A jewelry store owner said the quantity of raw diamonds he wants to buy follows the logarithmic value of one more than the total carat weight of the diamond, as shown in the graph below. Which statement is true about the graph?

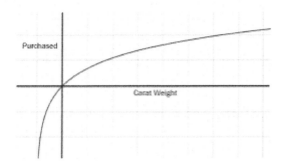

 Ⓐ Since the graph goes through the origin, the owner does not want to buy any 2 carat diamonds.

 Ⓑ Since the graph goes through the origin, the owner does not want to buy any 1 carat diamonds.

 Ⓒ The owner is not willing to buy a diamond of less than 1.8 carat weight.

 Ⓓ Since the graph goes through the origin, there aren't any 1 carat diamonds.

4. In which scenario would a person's level of mathematical accuracy be the most crucial?

 Ⓐ A carpet-fitter installing new carpet in one's house

 Ⓑ An engineer determining the maximum capacity of a bridge

 Ⓒ Mechanic changing the oil in a car

 Ⓓ A calculus student finding a derivative

5. Given a line with slope of 100, what would be the best scale to use for the x and y axis? What should you count by on the x and y axis to show this graph most accurately?

 Ⓐ 100 for x, 1 for y

 Ⓑ 100 for x, 100 for y

 Ⓒ 1 for x, 1 for y

 Ⓓ 1 for x, 100 for y

6. You need exactly 10 kg of corn or rice. The store has corn for $15 for 2 kg and rice for $20 for 3 kg. What is the least you must spend to buy exactly 10 kg?

 Ⓐ 55

 Ⓑ 60

 Ⓒ 70

 Ⓓ 75

7. Which of the following would save more gas over a year? Assume the owner of the car drives it 12,000 miles per year.

   Ⓐ Replacing a car that can travel 20 miles per gallon with a car that can travel 25 miles per gallon

   Ⓑ Replacing a car that can travel 16 miles per gallon with a car that can travel 24 miles per gallon

   Ⓒ Replacing a car that can travel 25 miles per gallon with a car that can travel 32 miles per gallon

   Ⓓ Replacing a car that can travel 12 miles per gallon with a car that can travel 20 miles per gallon

8. Angelica is going to drive from Dallas, TX to Mexico City to visit family. The trip is just over 1130 miles long. How long can she expect to be driving in hours?

   Ⓐ 20 hrs
   Ⓑ 45 hrs
   Ⓒ 5 hrs
   Ⓓ 29 hrs

9. Angie loves math and is enamored with Albert Einstein. She learns that Einstein died in 1955 and he was in his 70's. What is a reasonable estimate for the year he was born?

   Ⓐ 1875
   Ⓑ 1900
   Ⓒ 1877
   Ⓓ 1890

10. A football field including the two end zones measures 160 feet wide and 360 feet long. If we allow each person 4.2 square feet of personal space, approximately how many people can we fit on the field at one time?

   Ⓐ 14,000
   Ⓑ 13,714.29
   Ⓒ 50,000
   Ⓓ 25,000

11. Which measurement is the most precise?

Ⓐ 48 km
Ⓑ 480 hm
Ⓒ 4800 dm
Ⓓ 48,000 m

12. The rectangular base of a manufacturing machine has a length of 8.4 ft. and a width of 3 ± 0.4 ft. What is the range of the area of the base of the machine?

Ⓐ [21.84, 28.56]
Ⓑ [25.2, 28.56]
Ⓒ [21.84, 29.92]
Ⓓ [20.8, 28.56]

13. Jennifer has a jar full of quarters she has been saving. Every year she saves quarters from January until the end of November. She then cashes out her quarters and uses the money to help buy Christmas presents for her children. Which would provide Jennifer with a good estimate for the amount of money she has in her jar?

Ⓐ Calculating the volume of the jar
Ⓑ Counting all the coins
Ⓒ Weighing the jar
Ⓓ Setting up a proportion between the height of the jar she is using this year and the amount last year's jar yielded along with its height

14. Cathie is on a diet. She is using an app on her phone to track how many calories she eats for each meal and snack. Which of the following might have about the same number of calories as Cathie's meal?

Ⓐ A hamburger patty from the local burger joint
Ⓑ An apple
Ⓒ A diet coke
Ⓓ An order of cheese fries

15. Janet is planning to run a 5k race. If a 5k converts to about 3.1 miles, and there are 63,360 inches in a mile, about how many inches will Janet be running?

Ⓐ 196,416 inches
Ⓑ 200,000 inches
Ⓒ 250,000 inches
Ⓓ 190, 000 inches

Chapter 3 - Seeing Structure in Expressions

1. **Which of the following is an expression with a degree of 7, leading coefficient of 2 and a constant of negative 8?**

   Ⓐ $-8x^7 - x^2 - 2$
   Ⓑ $2x^5 - x^2 - 8$
   Ⓒ $2x^7 - x^2 - 8$
   Ⓓ $-8x^5 - x^2 - 2$

2. **What expression represents the number of inches in x feet?**

   Ⓐ $\dfrac{x}{12}$

   Ⓑ $12x$

   Ⓒ $\dfrac{12}{x}$

   Ⓓ None of these

3. **What is the coefficient of the second term in the expression $7x^2y^2 + 3xy - 25$?**

   Ⓐ 7
   Ⓑ 4
   Ⓒ -25
   Ⓓ 3

4. **What is the coefficient of the third term the expression $5x^3y^4 + 7x^2y^3 - 6xy^2 - 8xy$?**

   Ⓐ 6
   Ⓑ 7
   Ⓒ -8
   Ⓓ -6

5. **The formula $P(1+r)^t$ is used to calculate the amount in an account that earns interest, compounded annually. In the expression, P is the principal in the account, r is the annual interest rate as a decimal, and t is the time in years. What is the interest rate in the expression 500(1.025)?**

   Ⓐ 1.5%
   Ⓑ 2.5%
   Ⓒ 1.025%
   Ⓓ 25%

6. Which expression is equivalent to $16x^4 - 9x^2$?

Ⓐ $(4x^2 - 3x)^2$
Ⓑ $(4x^2 + 3x)^2$
Ⓒ $(4x^2 + 3x)(4x^2 - 3x)$
Ⓓ $(4x^2 - x)(4x^2 - 9x)$

7. Which expression is equivalent to $15x^6 - 5x^4$?

Ⓐ $5(3x^2 - 1)$
Ⓑ $5x^2(3x^2 - 1)^2$
Ⓒ $5x^4(3x^2 - 1)$
Ⓓ $5(3x^2 - 1)^4$

8. Which expression is equivalent to $9x^2 - 16y^2$?

Ⓐ $(3x - 4y)(3x - 4y)$
Ⓑ $(3x + 4y)(3x + 4y)$
Ⓒ $(3x + 4y)(3x - 4y)$
Ⓓ $(3x - 4y)^2$

9. The greatest common factor of $4a^2b$ and $8a^3b^2$ is:

Ⓐ $2a^2b$
Ⓑ $4a^2b^2$
Ⓒ $8a^3b^2$
Ⓓ $4a^2b$

10. Which expression is equivalent to $c(x^3 - 3y) + c(4x^3 - 4y)$?

Ⓐ $5cx^3 - 7cy$
Ⓑ $c(5x^3 + 7y)$
Ⓒ $2c(5x^3 - 7y)$
Ⓓ $5cx^3 + 7cy$

11. Factor the quadratic function $f(x) = 9x^2 + 66x + 21$. What are the zeros?

Ⓐ $\frac{1}{3}, 7$

Ⓑ $-\frac{1}{3}, -7$

Ⓒ $-3, -7$
Ⓓ $-1, -7$

12. Factor the quadratic function $k(p)=5p2+19p+12$. What are the zeros?

Ⓐ $\frac{4}{5}, 3$

Ⓑ $-\frac{4}{5}, 3$

Ⓒ $\frac{4}{5}, -3$

Ⓓ $-\frac{4}{5}, -3$

13. Which is the solution set of the equation $(x-3)(x+2)=0$?

Ⓐ 3 and - 2
Ⓑ 3 and 2
Ⓒ - 3 and 2
Ⓓ - 3 and - 2

14. A study of fish in a man-made lake in Florida showed there was a population decrease of 25% over a decade. The model used to was $P=420(.75)^d$, where d is the decades after 2010, and P is the population in thousands. A new study would like to predict the population after y years. Which equation below can be used for the prediction?

Ⓐ $P=420(.0563)^y$
Ⓑ $P=420(.9716)^y$
Ⓒ $P=420(.9750)^y$
Ⓓ $P=420(.6501)^y$

15. What is the solution set of the equation $2x^2-4x=6$?

Ⓐ $\{-1, -3\}$
Ⓑ $\{1, 3\}$
Ⓒ $\{1, -3\}$
Ⓓ $\{-1, 3\}$

Chapter 4 - Arithmetic with Polynomials

1. Add these polynomials. $(9x^3 + 2x^2 - 4x + 1) + (-5x^3 - x^2 - 5x + 7)$

- Ⓐ $5x^3+3x^2-9x+8$
- Ⓑ $4x^3+x^2-7x+9$
- Ⓒ $14x^3+3x^2-9x+8$
- Ⓓ $4x^3+x^2-9x+8$

2. Multiply these polynomials. $(3x^3 + 4x^2) * (-3x^2+2x+1)$

- Ⓐ $-9x^5+11x^3+4x^2$
- Ⓑ $9x^5+6x^4+11x^3+4x^2$
- Ⓒ $9x^5-6x^4-11x^3+4x^2$
- Ⓓ $-9x^5-6x^4+11x^3+4x^2$

3. Add these polynomials. $(x^3-x^2-14x+8) + (x^3-5x^2+7x+2)$

- Ⓐ $2x^3-6x^2-14x+8$
- Ⓑ $2x^3-6x^2-7x+10$
- Ⓒ $2x^3-5x^2+8$
- Ⓓ $2x^3-6x^2+4$

4. The expression $6a^2 - 3a + (-14a^2) - 6a + 12a^2$ **is equivalent to**

- Ⓐ $5a^2$
- Ⓑ $-5a^2$
- Ⓒ $-4a^4 -9a^2$
- Ⓓ $4a^2 - 9a$

5. Which answer choice expresses the difference of $(4x^2 + 2x - 3) - (2x^2 - 5x - 1)$?

- Ⓐ $2x^2 - 3x - 2$
- Ⓑ $2x^2 + 7x - 2$
- Ⓒ $2x^2 - 3x - 4$
- Ⓓ $2x^2 + 7x - 4$

6. Which expression can be used to find the distance traveled in 5 hours by a bus traveling at 4x - 2 miles per hour?

Ⓐ $\dfrac{4x - 2}{5}$

Ⓑ 5(4x) + 5(2)

Ⓒ 5(4x - 2)

Ⓓ none of these

Chapter 5 - Creating Equations

1. Ms. Baker is making cookies for her family's holiday party. Her favorite recipe calls for 2 cups of flour and ½ cup of chocolate chips. She accidentally put in 3 cups of flour, how many chocolate chips will she need to ensure the cookies come out correctly?

   Ⓐ $\frac{3}{4}$ cup

   Ⓑ $\frac{1}{3}$ cup

   Ⓒ $\frac{1}{8}$ cup

   Ⓓ 1 cup

2. Simeon is two years older than Brina. The product of their ages is 63. If *b*, represents Brina's age, which equation below can be used to find Simeon's age?

   Ⓐ b(b + 2) = 63
   Ⓑ s+b+2 = 63
   Ⓒ s(b+2) = 63
   Ⓓ None of these

3. Madison is a sales associate for a transportation options dealer. Each month she sells two cars for every 10 bicycles and four motorcycles for every car. If she makes 40 sales per month, and the variable x represents the number of cars she sells, which equation could you use to find how many cars she sells?

   Ⓐ x+5x+4x=40
   Ⓑ x+5x+4x=20
   Ⓒ 2x+10x+8x=40
   Ⓓ 2x+10x+8x=20

4. Joanie bought 12 books. The total cost of the books, with tax, was $215.88. Joanie gave three of the books to the local community library. What was the value of the three books she donated?

   Ⓐ $17.99
   Ⓑ $35.98
   Ⓒ $53.97
   Ⓓ $71.96

5. A store's policy states that no more than 16 teenagers can be inside the store at any time. If there are 4 boys and 7 girls inside the store right now, which group of teenagers would not be allowed to enter the store?

   Ⓐ Two boys and three girls
   Ⓑ Two boys and one girl
   Ⓒ Six boys and two girls
   Ⓓ One girl and four boys

6. Pete's School Supply Shop has a big back to school special. For $25, you get 7 folders, 5 packs of paper, 8 pens, and 15 pencils. How much does a pack of paper cost if folders cost $0.85, pens cost $1.20, and pencils cost $0.45?

   Ⓐ $0.54
   Ⓑ $0.45
   Ⓒ $0.75
   Ⓓ $0.35

7. Which equation demonstrates a direct variation of x and y, if when x = 4, y = 20?

   Ⓐ $y = x + 16$
   Ⓑ $y = 5x$
   Ⓒ $x = 5y$
   Ⓓ $x = y - 16$

8. A hot air balloon leaves the ground rising at a steady rate of 3 kilometers (k) per minute (m). Which equation below represents this relationship?

   Ⓐ $k = 3 + m$
   Ⓑ $k = 3m$
   Ⓒ $m = 3k$
   Ⓓ $m = k + 3$

9. Which equation uses the function rule for the values in the table below?

X	f(x)
6	19
7	23
8	27

   Ⓐ $f(x)=5x-4$
   Ⓑ $f(x)=4x-5$
   Ⓒ $f(x)=4x+5$
   Ⓓ $f(x)=3x+1$

10. Which equation uses the function rule for the values in the table below?

X	f(x)
14	31
15	40
16	49

Ⓐ f(x)=9x-95
Ⓑ f(x)=8x-75
Ⓒ f(x)=4x+95
Ⓓ f(x)=15x-109

11. Which equation uses the function rule for the values in the table below?

X	f(x)
25	48
26	50
27	52

Ⓐ f(x)=2x-2
Ⓑ f(x)=4x-2
Ⓒ f(x)=-2x+2
Ⓓ f(x)=-2x+104

12. Which equation uses the function rule for the values in the table below?

X	f(x)
6	2
7	8
8	14

Ⓐ f(x)=4x-44
Ⓑ f(x)=6x-36
Ⓒ f(x)=6x-34
Ⓓ f(x)=-6x+34

13. The ratio of staff to guests at the gala was 3 to 5. There were a total of 576 people in the ballroom. How many guests were at the gala?

Ⓐ 216
Ⓑ 360
Ⓒ 300
Ⓓ 276

14. Verizon wireless charges a set fee of $55, for it's basic plan which includes several 3 gigabytes of data. If a customer goes over their data plan and uses more than the 3 gigabytes, they are charged an additional $40. If V represents the cost of and d represents the total number of gigabytes of data, which equation would represent the bill for a customer who went over their plan?

Ⓐ V = 55 + 40(d - 3)
Ⓑ V = 55 + 40(3 - d)
Ⓒ V = 40 + 55(d - 3)
Ⓓ V = 40 + 55(3 - d)

15. A new factory opened with 12 production workers and 6 support people on the staff. The company intends to hire 18 production workers and 24 support people per month until the factory has its full staff of 480 factory workers. How many months will that take?

Ⓐ 12
Ⓑ 27
Ⓒ 11
Ⓓ 20

16. The student council is holding a dance for the school. The council pays $420 to rent a local firehouse ball for the evening. The council must also pay $2 per guest that at tends for insurance. If the council charges $8 per ticket for the dance, how many tickets must they sell in order to recover all of the costs for the facility?

Ⓐ 60
Ⓑ 70
Ⓒ 53
Ⓓ 52

17. Drake and Heidi meet in the keyboarding lab to type their term paper assignments. Drake can type at a speed of 45 words per minute and Heidi can type at a speed of 60 words per minute. What are the combined minutes of typing they will have to do if Drake's term paper is 2160 words and Heidi's term paper is 2,640 words?

Ⓐ 44
Ⓑ 92
Ⓒ 48
Ⓓ 46

18. Bryan needs a cheap courier service to deliver holiday gifts to his brother. The first courier service charges a flat fee of $18 plus $6 per pound. The second courier service charges a flat fee of $20 plus $5 per pound. If Bryan determines that the second courier service will be cheaper, how many pounds will Bryan ship?

Ⓐ Two
Ⓑ Less than or equal two
Ⓒ Greater than two
Ⓓ Cannot be determined

19. The formula for the area of a triangle is A= $\frac{1}{2}$ bh. Solve for b.

Ⓐ $b = \dfrac{A}{2h}$

Ⓑ $b = \dfrac{2A}{h}$

Ⓒ $b = 2Ah$

Ⓓ $b = \dfrac{Ah}{2}$

20. Ohm's Law states $P = \dfrac{E^2}{R}$. Solve for E.

Ⓐ $E=PR^2$
Ⓑ $E=PR$
Ⓒ $E=P^2R$
Ⓓ $E = \sqrt{PR}$

21. The Perimeter formula for a triangle is P=a+b+c, solve for c.

Ⓐ c=P−(a+b)
Ⓑ c=P−a−b
Ⓒ c=P−a+b
Ⓓ a and b

22. Solve the formula for r in $7 = \frac{r}{7}(2s - 5t)$.

Ⓐ $r = \dfrac{7}{2s - 5t}$

Ⓑ $r = \dfrac{49}{2s - 5t}$

Ⓒ $r = \dfrac{2s - 5t}{49}$

Ⓓ $r = 14s - 35tr = 14s - 35t$

23. Solve the formula for w in $2u = \frac{w}{5}(7x - 3y)$.

Ⓐ $w = \dfrac{5u}{7x - 3y}$

Ⓑ $w = 10u(7x - 3y)$

Ⓒ $w = 10u(7x + 3y)$

Ⓓ $w = \dfrac{10u}{7x - 3y}$

24. Solve the formula for q in $\frac{7r + 5s}{3q} = 8$.

Ⓐ $q = \dfrac{7r + 5s}{3}$

Ⓑ $q = \dfrac{7r + 5s}{8}$

Ⓒ $q = \dfrac{7r + 5s}{24}$

Ⓓ $q = 24 - 7r + 5s$

Chapter 6 - Reasoning with Equations and Inequalities

1. What is the solution to 8x-8=96?

   Ⓐ 19
   Ⓑ 13
   Ⓒ -13
   Ⓓ -19

2. If _a_ and _b_ are integers, which equation below will always be true?

   Ⓐ $\left(\frac{a}{b}\right)\left(-\frac{a}{b}\right)=-1$

   Ⓑ a+3b=b+3a
   Ⓒ a-1=b-1
   Ⓓ ab=ba

3. What is the solution to the equation $\frac{x}{5}-11=2$?

   Ⓐ $\frac{13}{5}$

   Ⓑ -65
   Ⓒ 56
   Ⓓ 65

4. In the set of positive integers, what is the solution set of the inequality 2x −3<5?

   Ⓐ {0,1,2,3}
   Ⓑ {1,2,3}
   Ⓒ {0,1,2,3,4}
   Ⓓ {1,2,3,4}

5. What are the solutions to the quadratic equation below?
     $2x^2-3x+1=0$

   Ⓐ -½, 1
   Ⓑ ½, 1
   Ⓒ ½, -1
   Ⓓ -½, -1

6. Solve the quadratic $-8p^2 = 40p$.

   Ⓐ 0, −5
   Ⓑ 0, 5
   Ⓒ −8, 40
   Ⓓ 8, −40

7. Use the elimination method to solve the system of equations.
   $5x+2y=0$
   $3x-2y=-16$

   Ⓐ (−5, 2)
   Ⓑ (2, −5)
   Ⓒ (−2, 5)
   Ⓓ (5, −2)

8. Solve the system of equations below by replacing one equation with the sum of the two equations or by a multiple of the equation, and then adding the two equations together.

   $2x-3y=7$
   $3x+y=5$

   Ⓐ (−1,2)
   Ⓑ (3,−4)
   Ⓒ (2,−1)
   Ⓓ (5,1)

9. Two cans of paint and one roller cost $62. Five cans of the same paint and two rollers cost $151. Find the cost of one can of paint and one roller.

   Ⓐ can of paint $27, one roller $8
   Ⓑ can of paint $8, one roller $27
   Ⓒ can of paint $25, one roller $12
   Ⓓ can of paint $30, one roller $2

10. Solve the system of equations by graphing the lines.
    $3x+y=4$
    $3x-y=2$

    Ⓐ (1,0)
    Ⓑ (1,2)
    Ⓒ (1,1)
    Ⓓ (2,1)

11. **Would this system of equations intersect? If so, how many times?**

$$y = x^2 + 5x + 9$$
$$y = \frac{1}{4}x - 8$$

Ⓐ Yes, one
Ⓑ No
Ⓒ Yes, two
Ⓓ Yes, three

12. **Solve this system of a quadratic equation and a linear equation algebraically.**
$$x^2 + y^2 = 36$$
$$x = 4$$

Ⓐ $(4, 2\sqrt{5})$

Ⓑ $(4, \pm 2\sqrt{5})$

Ⓒ $(\pm 2\sqrt{5}, 4)$

Ⓓ $(4, -2\sqrt{5})$

13. **Which function contains the point (6,2)?**

Ⓐ $f(x) = -\frac{2}{3}x + 11$

Ⓑ $f(x) = -\frac{3}{2}x + 16$

Ⓒ $f(x) = -\frac{3}{2}x + 11$

Ⓓ $f(x) = -x + 9$

14. **At what point, in the first quadrant, do the two functions $f(x) = x^2 + 8x - 15$ and $g(x) = -x^2 + 4x + 15$ intersect?**

Ⓐ $(3, 18)$
Ⓑ $(-5, -30)$
Ⓒ $(18, 3)$
Ⓓ $(-30, -5)$

15. The projected budget of your company this year compared to last year is projected to be a linear inequality. The inequalities are $y \leq 2x$ and $y \geq -0.25x + 6$. If x represents days, after how many days will the two budgets overlap?

Ⓐ After 3 days
Ⓑ In less than 1 days
Ⓒ In less than 2 days
Ⓓ In less than 3 days

Chapter 7 - Interpreting Functions

1. Given the following table of values, identify the range.

X	Y
3	12
10	25
-1	5
9	20
0	9

Ⓐ {−1, 0, 3, 9, 10}
Ⓑ {5, 9, 12, 20, 25}
Ⓒ {5, 9, 12, 20}
Ⓓ {5, 12, 20, 25}

2. Given the function $h(x)=x^2-9x-33$, what is the range of $h(x)$ if the domain is {21,22,23,24}?

Ⓐ {219,253,289,327}
Ⓑ {119,153,189,227}
Ⓒ {219,253,289,336}
Ⓓ {219,263,299,327}

3. Suppose the function $f(x)$ cubes the input and then adds 9. What is $f(4)$?

Ⓐ 25
Ⓑ 73
Ⓒ 64
Ⓓ 55

4. Which statement best describes the function notation $f(x + 2) = -3$?

Ⓐ The output is -3 when the input is 2
Ⓑ The output is x+2 when the input is -3
Ⓒ The output is -3 when the input is x+2
Ⓓ None of these

5. **What is the recursive formula for this arithmetic sequence? 5,19,33,47, ...**

   Ⓐ $a_n = a_{n-1} + 14$
   Ⓑ $a_n = a_{n-1} \times 14$
   Ⓒ $a_n = a_{n-1} + 5$
   Ⓓ $a_n = 14 + 5(n-1)$

6. **What is the 15ᵗʰ number of the sequence (13, 11, 9, 7 . . .)**

   Ⓐ -17
   Ⓑ -13
   Ⓒ -15
   Ⓓ -11

7. **The line graph below shows the number of people at a music event from the time the gate opened to hours later. What does the graph in the interval from 3 hours to 5 hours show?**

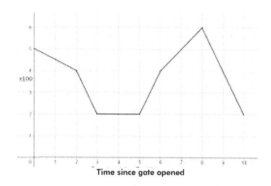

   Time since gate opened

   Ⓐ The maximum number of people at the event remains at 600
   Ⓑ The minimum number of people at the event remained steady at 200
   Ⓒ 500 people were at the event when the gate opened
   Ⓓ 200 people were at the event when the gate closed

8. **Describe the end behavior of the function y = 3x² + 6.**

   Ⓐ As $x \to -\infty$, $y \to \infty$ and as $x \to \infty$, $y \to \infty$
   Ⓑ As $x \to -\infty$, $y \to -\infty$ and as $x \to \infty$, $y \to \infty$
   Ⓒ As $x \to -\infty$, $y \to \infty$ and as $x \to \infty$, $y \to -\infty$
   Ⓓ As $x \to -\infty$, $y \to -\infty$ and as $x \to \infty$, $y \to -\infty$

9. The function $f(x) = -\frac{1}{8}\left(x - \frac{7}{2}\right)^2 + \frac{3}{2}$ is the path of a football at a practice game. Its graph is shown below. What portion of the domain of this function actually models this situation?

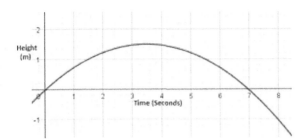

Ⓐ [7,0]
Ⓑ [−1,7]
Ⓒ (−∞,∞)
Ⓓ [0,7]

10. You have a savings of $500. You can choose to either add to or subtract from this savings. What is the domain of money, m, you can add or remove from your savings?

Ⓐ −500≤m≤500
Ⓑ m≥0
Ⓒ m≥−500
Ⓓ m≤500

11. Values of a function are given in the table below. What is the average rate of change of the function on the interval [5,20]?

x	f(x)
5	-7
10	4
15	15
20	26

Ⓐ $-\frac{11}{5}$

Ⓑ $\frac{11}{5}$

Ⓒ $\frac{5}{11}$

Ⓓ $-\frac{5}{11}$

12. Calculate the average rate of change of $g(x) = \frac{1}{2x} - x^2$ between x=−1 and x=5, as a function of x.

   Ⓐ -6.6
   Ⓑ -5.85
   Ⓒ -4.4
   Ⓓ -3.9

13. The graph of a transformed square root curve is in the figure below. What is the equation of the curve?

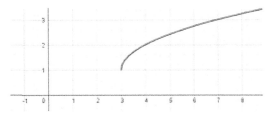

   Ⓐ $y = \sqrt{x + 3} + 1$
   Ⓑ $y = \sqrt{x - 3} + 1$
   Ⓒ $y = \sqrt{x - 3}$
   Ⓓ $y = \sqrt{x + 3}$

14. Which function is that is equivalent to $h(x)=x^4-3x^3-4x^2$ and allows us to find the zeros of the function?

   Ⓐ $h(x)=x^2(x^2-3x-4)$
   Ⓑ $h(x)=x(x^2-4x)(x+1)$
   Ⓒ $h(x)=x^2(x-4)(x+1)$
   Ⓓ $h(x)=x(x-4)(x^2+x)$

15. Two functions are represented in different ways:
The table shows values of h(x), which is a quadratic function.

x	h(x)
3	1
6	4
9	9
12	16

The function k(x), which is a linear function, is k(x)=2x-7. Which function grows at a faster rate between x=3 and x=9?

Ⓐ h(x)
Ⓑ They grow at the same rate
Ⓒ k(x)
Ⓓ It's impossible to tell

Chapter 8 - Building Functions

1. The value of the output variable of a function is always 7 less than the square of the input variable. If the relationship is expressed as ordered pairs (g,h), what is the function?

   Ⓐ $f(g)=7-g^3$
   Ⓑ $f(g)=g^3+7$
   Ⓒ $f(g)=g^3-7$
   Ⓓ $f(g)=g^2-7$

2. Which function correctly describes the relationship between a and b in the table below, with a as the independent variable?

a	1	2	3	4
b	4	8	12	16

   Ⓐ $f(b) = 4a$
   Ⓑ $f(a) = \dfrac{a}{4}$
   Ⓒ $f(a) = 4a$
   Ⓓ $f(b) = \dfrac{b}{4}$

3. Given the function $h(t)=-1.3t^2+5t$, representing the height in terms of time for the potential energy equation PE=mgh, at what point in time is PE the highest? What is this value in terms of mg? Round all decimals to the nearest hundredth.

   Ⓐ t=1.92, PE=4.81mg
   Ⓑ t=2, PE=4.8mg
   Ⓒ t=1, PE=3.7mg
   Ⓓ Not enough information

4. Write a symbolic function describing the distance traveled by an boat as a function of headwind and forward speed.

   Ⓐ Distance = (Speed−Headwind) * Time Traveled
   Ⓑ Distance = (Speed+Headwind) * Time Traveled
   Ⓒ Distance = Speed * Headwind * Time Traveled
   Ⓓ None of these

5. Your allowance increases by $2.50 every year and you start at $10 the first year. Which could represent your allowance as a function of years.

  Ⓐ $F(n)=10.00+2.50n$
  Ⓑ $F(n)=7.50+2.50n$
  Ⓒ $F(n)=7.50n+2.50$
  Ⓓ $F(n)=10.00n+2.50$

6. What is the explicit function of the sequence given by the function
  $f(n)=f_{n-1}+4$, with $f_1=0$?

  Ⓐ $f(n)=4n+4$
  Ⓑ $f(n)=4n$
  Ⓒ $f(n)=4n-4$
  Ⓓ None of these

7. Your cable bill increases by $5 each year starting with the discount price of $39.99 for the first year. Which could represent your cable bill as a function of years.

  Ⓐ $C(y)=39.99+5y$
  Ⓑ $C(y)=39.99y+5$
  Ⓒ $C(y)=39.99-5y$
  Ⓓ $C(y)=39.99y-5$

8. If the 8th term of a sequence represented by the recursive function $f(n) = 2f_{n-1}+ 3$ is 509, What is the 9th term?

  Ⓐ 253
  Ⓑ 1018
  Ⓒ 1021
  Ⓓ None of these

9. How is the graph of $f(x) = x + 7$ different from $g(x) = x + 12$?

  Ⓐ When f(x) is shifted up 5 units, g(x) will be obtained
  Ⓑ g(x) is obtained by shifting f(x) down 5 units
  Ⓒ When g(x) is shifted up 5 units, f(x) will be obtained
  Ⓓ f(x) is obtained by shifting g(x) up 5 units

10. Describe how $f(x)=(x-3)^2$ is different from $g(x) = (x+3)^2$.

Ⓐ The graph of f(x) is a parabola shifted 3 units left, while the graph of g(x) is a parabola shifted 3 units right.

Ⓑ The graph of f(x) is a parabola shifted 3 units up, while the graph of g(x) is a parabola shifted 3 units down.

Ⓒ The graph of f(x) is a parabola shifted 3 units right, while the graph of g(x) is a parabola shifted 3 units left.

Ⓓ The graph of f(x) is a parabola shifted 3 units down, while the graph of g(x) is a parabola shifted 3 units up.

11. How do the graphs of $f(x) = \sin(x)$ and $g(x) = 3\sin(x)$ relate to each other? In other words how could you obtain the graph of g(x) from f(x)?

Ⓐ Vertical shrink by a factor of 3

Ⓑ Vertical stretch by a factor of $\frac{1}{3}$

Ⓒ Vertical stretch by a factor of 3
Ⓓ None of these

12. How can you sketch the graph of $y = (x - 2)^2 + 3$ from the graph $y = -4x^2$?

Ⓐ Reflect over the x-axis, vertically shrink by a factor of 4, shift 3 units up, and 2 units to the left
Ⓑ Reflect over the x-axis, shift 3 units up, and 2 units to the right
Ⓒ Vertically shrink by a factor of 4, shift 3 units up, and 2 units to the right
Ⓓ Reflect over the x-axis, vertically shrink by a factor of 4, shift 3 units up, and 2 units to the right

13. Find $f^{-1}(x)$ when $f(x)=7x-1$.

Ⓐ 7x + 1

Ⓑ -7x + 1

Ⓒ $\frac{x+1}{7}$

Ⓓ $\frac{x-1}{7}$

14. **What is the inverse of the function f(x) =3^x ?**

   Ⓐ f^{-1}(x) = log$_3$x
   Ⓑ f^{-1}(x) = logx
   Ⓒ f^{-1}(x) = x^2
   Ⓓ Inverse does not exist

15. **In order to make f(x) = x^2 an invertible function, its domain should be which of the following?**

   Ⓐ x ≥ 0
   Ⓑ x ≤ 0
   Ⓒ x ≠ 0
   Ⓓ x ∈ R

Chapter 9 - Linear, Quadratic, and Exponential Models

1. One dollar is invested in an account that accumulates 20% interest every year. What type of function would represent this situation?

   Ⓐ Linear
   Ⓑ Quadratic
   Ⓒ Exponential growth
   Ⓓ Exponential decay

2. The temperature began at 2°C and decreases 5°C each hour. What type of function would represent this situation?

   Ⓐ Linear
   Ⓑ Quadratic
   Ⓒ Exponential growth
   Ⓓ Exponential decay

3. Which would complete this sentence accurately. An exponential function...

   Ⓐ Grows quickly
   Ⓑ Grows by an equal interval
   Ⓒ Grows by an equal factor
   Ⓓ None of the above

4. The difference between intervals in a linear function do which of the following?

   Ⓐ Stays the same
   Ⓑ Increases at a constant rate
   Ⓒ Decreases at a constant rate
   Ⓓ All of the above

5. Which arithmetic sequence rule produces the term values shown in the table below?

n	1	2	3	4
a	5	10	15	20

   Ⓐ $a_n = 5n$
   Ⓑ $a_n = 10n - 5$
   Ⓒ $a_n = n + 4$
   Ⓓ $a_n = 4n + 3$

6. Which function provides the values in the table below?

x	1	2	3	4
y	1	4	9	16

  Ⓐ $f(x) = x^2$

  Ⓑ $f(x) = x^3$

  © $f(x) = 2x$

  Ⓓ $f(x) = \frac{1}{4}x^4$

7. Which of the following is an exponential function?

  Ⓐ $y = 2x^2 + 4$

  Ⓑ $y = x^3$

  © $y = 2x - 5^3$

  Ⓓ $y = 4^x - 1$

8. Jane is training to run a 5K race. She has been charting her heart rate. Her resting heart rate is 60 beats per minute. After each minute, her heart-rate increases to 70, then 80, then 90. Write an equation to represent this situation.

  Ⓐ $f(x) = 10x + 50$

  Ⓑ $f(x) = 60x + 10$

  © $f(x) = 10x + 60$

  Ⓓ   None of these

9. One of the functions below will eventually surpass the other two. Which one?

  Ⓐ $y = x^{100}$

  Ⓑ $y = 100^x$

  © $y = 100x$

10. Which of these is a linear function?

  Ⓐ $y = ab^x$

  Ⓑ $y = mx + b$

  © $y = a^x$

  Ⓓ $y = ax^2 + bx + c$

11. A quadratic function is just a variant of a polynomial function. Is this statement true or false?

    Ⓐ True
    Ⓑ True when x≥0
    Ⓒ True when the a-value is positive
    Ⓓ False

12. Which of the following is possible if the function y=x+25 is surpassed by the function y=.5^x?

    Ⓐ x≥−5
    Ⓑ x≤−5
    Ⓒ x≤0
    Ⓓ None of these

13. Suppose there are 950 widgets in a warehouse when a new business opened. The business expects to sell 45 of the widgets per week. Which function I(w) represents the number of widgets that will be in the warehouse after selling them for w weeks?

    Ⓐ I(w)=−950+45w
    Ⓑ I(w)=950−45w
    Ⓒ I(w)=950+45w
    Ⓓ I(w)=45−950w

14. Suppose an amateur theater spent $565 to produce a play. The tickets to see the play cost $35 each. A member of the cast wrote function P(t) to represent the net profit of the play, with t representing the number of tickets sold. Which function correctly represents the net profit of the play?

    Ⓐ P(t)=− 35t+ 565
    Ⓑ P(t)= 35t+ 565
    Ⓒ P(t)= 35t− 565
    Ⓓ P(t)= 565t− 35

15. The ABC Early Childhood Center will open for business with 64 students. Every year after opening the school expects to add 26 new students. Which function S(x) represents the number of students who will be enrolled at the school after x years?

    Ⓐ S(x)=-26+64x
    Ⓑ S(x)=64+26x
    Ⓒ S(x)=64-26x
    Ⓓ S(x)=64x+26

Chapter 10 - Interpreting Categorical and Quantitative Data

1. Which line plot correctly displays the same information as the number set below?
   {3,6,7,3,5,8,3,5,4,8,6,7,5,5,4,8,6}

Ⓐ

Ⓑ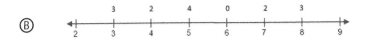

Ⓒ

Ⓓ

2. Below is a dot plot showing the scores students made on a quiz. Which of the following statements is true based on the dot plot?

Ⓐ One student made a score of 60.
Ⓑ More students scored a 90 than any other score.
Ⓒ 70 was the score received by the fewest students.
Ⓓ More students scored a 70 or 80 than scored a 90.

3. Which graphical form would be best to show how many students in David's class have different types of pets (dog, cat, bird).

(A) Box Plot
(B) Histogram
(C) Dot Plot
(D) All of the above would work equally well to represent the data

4. What is the difference between the medians of these two sets of numbers?
Set A: {6,8,10,12,14,16,18,20,22}
Set B: {3,5,7,9,11,13,15,17,19}

(A) 14
(B) 11
(C) 3
(D) 25

5. Below is a list of scores for a quiz. What is the upper quartile of the data?

| 71 | 82 | 92 | 99 | 100 | 75 | 85 | 79 | 95 | 87 | 86 | 81 |

(A) 92
(B) 95
(C) 93.5
(D) Cannot be calculated from the information given.

6. What is a unique characteristic of a set of data that is distributed normally?

(A) the mean is greater than the median
(B) the mean is less than the median
(C) the mean is the same as the median
(D) the data set does not have a median

7. A set of data has a mean and median that are equal. What must be true about the shape of the data?

(A) It is skewed to the left.
(B) It is skewed to the right.
(C) It is a mound.
(D) It is symmetrical.

8. A survey of 9th and 10th graders was conducted to see which type of pet they preferred. The result of the survey is in the table. Based on the survey, what is the probability that a student prefers a cat, given that the student is a 10th grader?

	Dog	Cat	Total
9th	32	17	49
10th	30	21	51
Total	62	38	100

Ⓐ $\frac{21}{100}$

Ⓑ $\frac{17}{38}$

Ⓒ $\frac{7}{17}$

Ⓓ $\frac{21}{38}$

9. Which of the following is an example of categorical data?

Ⓐ Maximum miles per hour a car can reach
Ⓑ Average miles / gallon of a car
Ⓒ Color of a car
Ⓓ Prices of different brands of cars

10. Given the scatter plot below, what type of function expresses the correlation between the two variables?

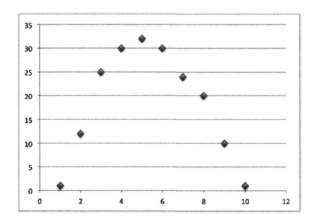

Ⓐ Linear
Ⓑ Exponential
Ⓒ Quadratic
Ⓓ Polar

11. Dr. Winthrop is conducting a study to test her hypothesis that the number of mosquitos in an area is dependent on the temperature. She believes the correlation is described by y=3x + 4.5. What does x represent in this equation?

Ⓐ The number of mosquitos in an area
Ⓑ The temperature
Ⓒ The total number of mosquitos counted throughout the study
Ⓓ A coefficient that creates a quadratic formula

12. John has a 10cm long orange candle. He lights the candle at noon. After three hours, the candle is 8cm long. Write a linear model that represents the length of the burning candle. What specifically does the slope in the equation represent in this scenario?

Ⓐ The candle is getting $\frac{2}{3}$ cm longer each hour

Ⓑ The candle is getting $\frac{2}{3}$ cm shorter each hour

Ⓒ The candle is getting 2cm shorter each hour
Ⓓ The candle is getting 2cm longer each hour

13. What is represented by the intercept (b) in the equation y=mx+b?

Ⓐ The maximum value of the function
Ⓑ The value when the dependent variable is zero
Ⓒ The value when the independent variable is zero
Ⓓ Both A and C

14. Research has hinted that when sales of ice cream increases, the violent crime rate and murder rate also increases. Is this a situation of correlation or a situation of causation?

Ⓐ correlation
Ⓑ causation
Ⓒ neither
Ⓓ impossible to tell

15. One year, swine flu because a possible epidemic in the US. Schools were closed for a week and the spread of the flu stopped almost immediately. Is the relationship between the number of swine flu cases and the closing of school for a week a correlation or causation?

Ⓐ correlation
Ⓑ causation
Ⓒ neither
Ⓓ impossible to tell

Answer Key
&
Detailed Explanations

Name: _____   Date: _____

Chapter 1 - Real Numbers

Question No.	Answer	Detailed Explanation
1	D	$49\frac{3}{2} = (\sqrt{49})^3 = (7)^3 = 7\times7\times7 = 343$ In a problem with a rational exponent, the numerator tells you the power, and the denominator the root. In this problem $49\frac{3}{2}$, the denominator is 2 so you would take the square root of 49, which equals 7. The numerator is 3 so you would do 7 to the 3rd power $(7\times7\times7)$ and that equals 343.
2	C	$9\frac{150}{300} = 9\frac{1}{2} = \sqrt{9} = 3$. In a problem with a rational exponent, the numerator tells you the power, and the denominator the root. However, in this problem the exponent can be reduced, so we should reduce that first. The exponent $\frac{150}{300} = \frac{1}{2}$. So the problem becomes 9 to the $\frac{1}{2}$ power. The denominator is 2 so we take the square root of 9 which is 3. The numerator is 1 so we raise 3 to the 1st power and the answer is 3.
3	C	The question asks for an equivalent simplified radical expression for $9^{\frac{2}{5}}$. A rational exponent can be rewritten using radicals because the denominator of the exponent is a root. Thus $9^{\frac{1}{5}} = \sqrt[5]{9}$. Then the radical expression is raised to the power of the numerator of the original rational exponent. Therefore, the number expression $9^{\frac{2}{5}} = (\sqrt[5]{9})^2$ or $\sqrt[5]{9^2}$.
4	B	The question asks for an equivalent expression for $(125^{\frac{3}{2}})^{\frac{4}{9}}$. First, use the exponent rule commonly referred to as the power of another power rule. This rule says to multiply the exponent in the given expression. Therefore, $(125^{\frac{3}{2}})^{\frac{4}{9}} = (125)^{\frac{3}{2}\cdot\frac{4}{9}} = (125)^{\frac{2}{3}}$. A rational exponent can be rewritten using radicals because the denominator of the exponent is a root. Thus $125^{\frac{1}{3}} = \sqrt[3]{125}$ and $\sqrt[3]{125} = 5$. Next, the numerator in the exponent means that you raise the base to that power. Therefore, the number expression $(125^{\frac{3}{2}})^{\frac{4}{9}} = (5)^2 = 25$.
5	D	The question asks for an equivalent radical expression for $(6^{\frac{1}{7}})^{\frac{7}{2}}$. First, use the exponent rule commonly referred to as the power of another power rule. This rule says to multiply the exponent in the given expression. Therefore, $(6^{\frac{1}{7}})^{\frac{7}{2}} = 6^{\frac{1}{7}\cdot\frac{7}{2}} = 6^{\frac{1}{2}}$. A rational exponent can be rewritten using radicals because the denominator of the exponent is a root. Thus $6^{\frac{1}{2}} = \sqrt{6}$.

Question No.	Answer	Detailed Explanation
6	B	The expression $\sqrt[a]{x^b}$ can be rewritten as $(x^b)^{\frac{1}{a}}$. This expression can be changed using the power of a power exponent rule, which states that when we raise an expression with a power to a power, we multiply the two exponents. Therefore, $(x^b)^{\frac{1}{a}} = x^{b \cdot \frac{1}{a}} = x^{\frac{b}{a}}$. Thus, $\sqrt[4]{x^3} = (x^3)^{\frac{1}{4}} = x^{3 \cdot \frac{1}{4}} = x^{\frac{3}{4}}$.
7	D	The expression $\sqrt[a]{x^b}$ can be rewritten as $(x^b)^{\frac{1}{a}}$. This expression can be changed using the power of a power exponent rule, which states that when we raise an expression with a power to a power, we multiply the two exponents. Therefore, $(x^b)^{\frac{1}{a}} = x^{b \cdot \frac{1}{a}} = x^{\frac{b}{a}}$. Thus, $\sqrt[7]{x^5 y^6} = (x^5 y^6)^{\frac{1}{7}} = x^{\frac{5}{7}} y^{\frac{6}{7}}$.
8	A	The expression $\sqrt[a]{x^b}$ can be rewritten as $(x^b)^{\frac{1}{a}}$. This expression can be changed using the power of a power exponent rule, which states that when we raise an expression with a power to a power, we multiply the two exponents. Therefore, $(x^b)^{\frac{1}{a}} = x^{b \cdot \frac{1}{a}} = x^{\frac{b}{a}}$. Thus, $[(abc)^9]^{\frac{1}{4}} = (abc)^{9 \cdot \frac{1}{4}} = (abc)^{\frac{9}{4}}$.
9	A	In a problem with a rational exponent, the numerator tells you the power, and the denominator the root. Since the problem is, $x^{\frac{1}{2}}$, the denominator is 2 indicating we should take a square root and the numerator is 1 so we would raise that to the first power or there will be no exponent since an exponent of 1 is rarely used. That makes the answer the square root of x, written as $\sqrt{x}$.
10	C	$1000^{\frac{2}{3}} = (\sqrt[3]{1000})^2 = (10)^2 = 100$ In a problem with a rational exponent, the numerator tells you the power, and the denominator the root. The answer for this problem is C because for $1000^{\frac{2}{3}}$ the denominator is 3 indicating that we would take the cube root of 1000 which is 10. The numerator is 2 indicating that we should raise 10 to the second power (10*10) which equals 100. In a problem that is worded like this it might also help to rule out the wrong answers in order to pick the correct answer. The following is an explanation as to why the other answer choices are not equal to 100. The correct answer for answer choice A is 10 because the cube root of 1000 is 10. Meaning that 10*10*10 = 1000. The correct answer for answer choice B is 1000, because the square root of 100 is 10, and if you cube 10 (10*10*10) you get 1000. The correct answer for answer choice D is a decimal answer or $10\sqrt{10}$ because 1000 is not a perfect square. The answer for this problem is C because the cube root of 1000 is 10 and 10 to the second power is 100.

Question No.	Answer	Detailed Explanation
11	D	Recall that a rational number is any number that can be expressed as a ratio or quotient of two integers (fractions). Both numbers can be expressed as fractions. The following steps show that $0.\overline{201}$ can be written as a fraction: $0.\overline{201} = \frac{201}{999} = \frac{67}{333}$. Now, add the two numbers: $\frac{67}{333} + \frac{2}{9} = \frac{67}{333} + \frac{2}{9} * \frac{37}{37} = \frac{67}{333} + \frac{74}{333} = \frac{141}{333} = \frac{47}{111}$. Since this number is expressed as a fraction, the sum is a rational number.
12	D	Recall that a rational number is any number that can be expressed as a ratio or quotient of two integers (fractions). The radical $\sqrt[4]{729}$ is a radical number that cannot be calculated exactly. Therefore, it is an irrational number and cannot be expressed as a fraction. The number $\frac{5}{7}$ is expressed as fractions and is a rational number. Multiply the two numbers together: $\frac{5}{7} * \sqrt[4]{729} = \frac{5\sqrt[4]{729}}{7}$. Since this number contains the original irrational number, the product is an irrational number.
13	D	Recall that a rational number is any number that can be expressed as a ratio or quotient of two integers (fractions). Irrational numbers are numbers that cannot be written as a fraction. This includes non-terminating, non-repeating decimals. The number 3.12112111211112... is a non-terminating, non-repeating decimal that cannot be changed to a fraction. Therefore, it is an irrational number. The number 3 can be expressed as the fractions $\frac{3}{1}$ and is a rational number. Multiply the two numbers together: 3*3.12112111211112=9.363363336333 36.... Since this product contains a non-terminating, non-repeating decimal, the product is an irrational number.
14	D	Recall that a rational number is any number that can be expressed as a ratio or quotient of two integers (fractions). Irrational numbers are numbers that cannot be expressed as a fraction. This includes non-terminating, non-repeating decimals. The number 2.123123412345123456... is a non-terminating, non-repeating decimal. Therefore, it is an irrational number. The number $\frac{25}{64}$ is a fraction, so it is a rational number which in decimal places becomes 0.390625. Adding these two we get, 2.5137..., irrational number.

Question No.	Answer	Detailed Explanation
15	B	$5\sqrt{3} - \sqrt{3} = (5 - 1)\sqrt{3} = 4\sqrt{3}$ Using the Subtraction rule for radicals, you can subtract the two coefficients (5 and an understood 1) to get a new coefficient of 4 and keep the radical $(\sqrt{3})$ the two terms have in common the same. The final result is $4\sqrt{3}$.

Chapter 2 - Quantities

Question No.	Answer	Detailed Explanation
1	B	At the origin, the aircraft is not moving. Since the drag is equal to a coefficient times the velocity, and the airplane is not moving, the velocity is zero. Thus, any coefficient times zero is zero. If the airplane is not moving, there is no drag.
2	A	Based on the information given, the driver was able to drive up to 70 miles per hour when not within a city. The graph shows that he/she did maintain that speed for about two hours. This speed equates to 7 grids along the y-axis. Therefore each mark (grid) represents 10 miles per hour.
3	C	The graph of a logarithmic function represents the quantity of diamonds the owner wants to buy, based on the carat weight of the diamond. The value at which the graph crosses y=1 is x=1.8. Therefore, the owner is not willing to buy diamonds less than 1.8 carat weight.
4	B	While all of these situations require some amount of accuracy, the word ``crucial'' implies that something life-threatening could happen if the calculations were off. The only situation that could risk people's lives would be an engineer determining the maximum capacity of a bridge. If he is off on his calculations, then the bridge could collapse causing life-threatening injuries or even death. All the other situations could be easily rectified if there was some error made in calculations.
5	D	We know that the slope of a line gives us $\frac{rise}{run}$. The numerator tells us how many units up the line goes and the denominator tells us how many units sideways the line goes. In this case, the line goes up 100 units for every 1 unit sideways. That means we want our x-axis to count by small numbers (or ones) and our y-axis to count by large numbers (or hundreds).
6	C	In order to buy exactly 10 kg of corn or rice, you must purchase two 2 kg packages of corn for $15 each and two 3 kg packages of rice for $20. The calculations are 2(2)kg+2(3)kg=10kg and 2(15)+2(20)= 70.

Question No.	Answer	Detailed Explanation
7	D	To find the car that would save the most gas, calculate the gas savings for each option. Replacing a car that can travel 20 miles per gallon with a car that can travel 25 miles per gallon 12,000÷20=600;12,000÷25=480; 120 gallons saved Replacing a car that can travel 16 miles per gallon with a car that can travel 24 miles per gallon 12,000÷16=750;12,000÷24=500; 250 gallons saved Replacing a car that can travel 25 miles per gallon with a car that can travel 32 miles per gallon 12,000÷25=480;12,000÷32=375; 105 gallons saved Replacing a car that can travel 12 miles per gallon with a car that can travel 20 miles per gallon 12,000÷12=1000;12,000÷20=600; 400 gallons saved
8	A	If we assume her average speed is 55 mph, then she would be driving for a little over 20 hours. If we assume her average speed is 75mph, then she would be driving for a little over 15 hours. Given this information and the fact that most speed limits are somewhere between 55 and 75 miles per hour, the only acceptable answer is 20. Choice C is much too small and the others are too large.
9	C	Earliest possible year 1955−79=1876, Latest possible year1955−70=1885 Using some logic we can conclude that the earliest possible year Einstein was born was 1876 and the latest possible year was 1885. We know Einstein died in his 70's and in the year 1955. That means he died somewhere between 70 and 79 years of age. If he died at 70, then the year he was born would be 1885 (1955 -- 70). If he did at 79, then the year he was born would be 1876 (1955 -- 79). If he died anywhere between 70 and 79 years of age (which he did since he was in his 70's), then he had to have died somewhere in the time period from 1876 to 1885. The only answer that falls in this time period is C, so that is the answer we would pick. It is the only ``reasonable'' answer. (The actual year that he was born is 1879, just so you know.)

Question No.	Answer	Detailed Explanation
10	A	160*360=57600÷4.2=13714.28571 If we do the calculations as shown we get answer choice B. This answer is wrong because we are giving an approximate number of people and it does not make sense to have a decimal representation of number of people. The answer must be a whole number. Answers C and D are much too large, leaving only answer choice A as a reasonable approximation.
11	C	48 km could be a measurement to the nearest 1,000 meters , 480 hm could be a measurement to the nearest 1,000 meters, and 4800 dm could be a measurement to the nearest 10 meters. The measurement of 48,000 m is measured to be to the nearest thousand meters, The most precise is 4800 dm.
12	A	The choices are in interval notation. To find the minimum area of the base, multiply 8.4*(3−0.4)=8.4*2.6=21.84 ft^2. To find the maximum area of the base, multiply 8.4*(3+0.4)=8.4*3.4=28.56 ft^2. Therefore, the range of the area of the base is [21.84, 28.56].
13	D	The most accurate way to tell how much money is in the jar is to count the money or take the money to the bank and let a machine count it. Since this problem only asks for a good estimate, we will not be choosing the method that would calculate the exact amount. So answer choice B is eliminated. Knowing how much the jar weighs or even how much it holds (its' volume) will not help us figure out an estimated amount. The most reasonable way to find an estimate is answer choice D.
14	A	An apple does not have enough calories to compare to the calories in an entire meal so answer choice B is wrong. Also answer C is nonsense because a diet coke should have zero calories so that would not compare the calories in a meal. An order of cheese fries could have any amount of fries and cheese included depending on where you get the fries from. So answer choice D is out because it's not specific enough. Answer choice A is the only one that would be a reasonable amount of calories.

Question No.	Answer	Detailed Explanation
15	B	The key to getting this estimation correct is noticing the word ``about'' before 3.1 miles. We can calculate the exact number of inches with the given values and we get answer choice A, but that is not the correct answer choice for this question. We only know the precision up to 0.1 miles or about 10,000 inches. That means we can only be precise up to the 10,000 inch point. Answer A is too specific. We need to round the exact answer to the nearest 10,000. In this case (196,416), the 6 in the thousands place tells the 9 in the ten thousands place to round up so we end up with 200,000.

Chapter 3 - Seeing Structure in Expressions

Question No.	Answer	Detailed Explanation
1	C	Student must demonstrate knowledge of the terms leading co-efficient, constant and degree; the leading coefficient is the number multiplied by the variable with the highest exponent, the degree is the highest exponent in the expression and a constant is a term with no variables (a number).
2	B	Student must know there are 12 inches in 1 foot and then further recognize that the number of feet needs to be multiplied by 12 in order to find out how many inches are in a given number of feet.
3	D	The expression $7x^2y^2+3xy-25$ is a trinomial expression, meaning it has three terms. The coefficient of a term is the number in the front of the term, whether or not the term has variables. The second term is 3xy and the number in the front of the term is 3.
4	D	The expression $5x^3y^4+7x^2y^3-6xy^2-8xy$ is a polynomial expression with four terms. The coefficient of a term is the number in the front of the term. If the term begins with a negative, then the coefficient is a negative number, whether or not the term has variables. The third term is $-6xy^2$ and the number in the front of the term is -6.
5	B	The question asks us what the interest rate is in the expression $500(1.025)^7$. This expression uses the formula $P(1+r)^t$ where r is the annual interest rate as a decimal. Therefore, we will write an equation and solve for r: $1.025=1+r$; $r=0.025$. Since r is the interest rate as a decimal, we will multiply our answer by 100 and add the percent symbol. The interest rate is $0.025*100=2.5\%$.
6	C	The given expression, $16x^4-9x^2$, is a difference of two squared terms. The formula for factoring a difference of squares is $a^2-b^2=(a+b)(a-b)$. Therefore, $16x^4-9x^2=(4x^2)^2-(3x)^2=(4x^2+3x)(4x^2-3x)$
7	C	The given expression, $15x^6-5x^4$, has a greatest common factor of $5x^4$, which can be factored out of the expression, giving us $15x^6-5x^4=5x^4(3x^2-1)$.

Question No.	Answer	Detailed Explanation
8	C	Student must recognize the expression is the difference of two perfect squares
9	D	Student must look at each term and find the greatest common factor (GCF) of each component of the term; the GCF of 4 and 8 is 4, the GCF of a^2 and a^3 is a^2, and the GCF of b and b^2 is b.
10	A	Student must distribute the c term to both binomials and then simplify by combining like terms.
11	B	The given quadratic function, $f(x)=9x^2+66x+21$, has a greatest common factor (GCF) of 3 . Start by factoring out the GCF: $f(x)=3(3x^2+22x+7)$. Next, factor the first and third terms so the factors give the middle coefficient when the binomials are multiplied using the FOIL process. Since all terms are positive, we know that all factors will have positive numbers. $f(x)=3(3x^2+22x+7)=3(3x+1)(x+7)$. Now, set the function equal to zero and use the zero product property to find the zeros of the function. $3(3x+1)(x+7)=0$; $3x+1=0$; $x+7=0$; Solving the two equations, we find that $x=-\frac{1}{3}$; $x=-7$.
12	D	First, we can see that since all of the terms are positive values, the expression must be factored into positive factors. We can also see that since the middle term has an odd coefficient, the third term must be factored into an odd factor and an even factor. Factor the first and third terms so the factors give the middle coefficient when the binomials are multiplied using the FOIL process. $k(p)=5p^2+19p+12=(5p+4)(p+3)$. Now, set the function equal to zero and use the zero product property to find the zeros of the function. $(5p+4)(p+3)=0;5p+4=0;p+3=0$. Solving the two equations, we find that $p=-\frac{4}{5}$; $p=-3$.
13	A	Student must solve for x by setting the factors equal to zero individually and then applying inverse operations
14	B	Student must recognize that the prediction in years requires a change be made to the growth/decay factor and then compute $(.75)^{1/10} \approx .9716$ to find the answer
15	D	Student must solve the quadratic any number of ways; the common approach to a problem like this is to set it equal to zero, then factor the GCF of 2, find the binomial factors (x-3)(x+1), and set each equal to zero to solve

Chapter 4 - Arithmetic with Polynomials

Question No.	Answer	Detailed Explanation
1	D	When combining polynomials, combine like terms by combining the coefficients. $(9x^3+2x^2-4x+1) + (-5x^3-x^2-5x+7)$ $(9x^3-5x^3) + (2x^2-x^2) + (-4x-5x) + (1+7)$ $4x^3+ x^2 -9x + 8$
2	D	When multiplying polynomials, use modified distribution and the product rule for exponents. Then, combine like terms by combining the coefficients. $(3x^3 + 4x^2) \cdot (-3x^2+2x+1)$ $3x^3 * (-3x^2+2x+1) + 4x^2 * (-3x^2+2x+1)$ $-9x^5 + 6x^4 + 3x^3 - 12x^4 + 8x^3 + 4x^2$ $-9x^5 - 6x^4 + 11x^3 + 4x^2$
3	B	When combining polynomials, combine like terms by combining the coefficients. $(x^3 - x^2 - 14x + 8) + (x^3 - 5x^2 + 7x + 2)$ $(x^3 + x^3) + (- x^2 + - 5x^2) + (-14x + 7x) + (8+2)$ $2x^3 - 6x^2 - 7x + 10$
4	D	Student must identify the like terms and combine by applying the rules for integer operations.
5	B	Student must identify the like terms and combine by applying the rules for integer operations; student must be careful to distribute the negative sign to the second polynomial
6	C	Student must recognize in order to find the distance, the monomial and the binomial must be multiplied.

Chapter 5 - Creating Equations

Question No.	Answer	Detailed Explanation
1	A	Student must set up a proportion $\dfrac{.5\ \text{cup choc}}{2\ \text{cups flour}} = \dfrac{x}{3\ \text{cups of flour}}$ and solve for x by cross multiplying and then dividing.
2	A	Student must define Simeon's age in terms of Brina's age as b + 2, then use the information given (product of the ages is 63) to set up the equation shown in answer choice a.
3	A	If we use the variable x for the number of cars Madison sells, and she sells two cars for every 10 bicycles, then she sells five times as many bicycles as cars. Thus she sells 5x bicycles. Then, if she sells four motor cycles for every car, the number of motorcycles she sells is 4x. The problem states that she makes 40 sales per month, so add the cars, bicycles, and motorcycles up and make that sum equal to 40. The equation is x+5x+4x=40.
4	C	If the 12 books cost $215.88, find the cost of each book with the equation 12x=215.88 where x is the cost of one book. Divide both sides by 12 and x=$17.99. Since Joan gave three books away, multiply x by three to find the value of these books. The cost of the three books was 3 × (17.99)=$53.97.
5	C	The problem states that no more than 16 teenagers can be inside the store at any time. If there are 4 boys and 7 girls inside the store right now, that means there are 11 teenagers in the store. Write an inequality that shows how many teenagers can enter the store: 11+x≤16 where x is the number of teenagers who can enter the store. Subtract 11 from both sides and x≤5. This means that any group that contains more than five teenagers will not be allowed to enter the store.
6	A	Write an equation using the given information and prices with x representing the cost of a pack of paper. 7(0.85)+5x+8(1.20)+15(0.45)=25 Multiply and combine like terms. 22.3+5x=25 Subtract 22.3 from both sides. 5x=2.70 Divide by 5:x=0.54 Each pack of paper costs $0.54.
7	B	Direct variation is represented by the equation y = kx, where k is the constant of variation; k≠0; student will find k to be 5 in this problem.

Question No.	Answer	Detailed Explanation
8	B	The number of kilometers reached, k, is a function of 3 times the number of minutes, m.
9	B	Begin by finding the slope of the line that contains the points. Use the points (6,19) and (8,27). The slope is $\frac{27-19}{8-6} = \frac{8}{2} = 4$. Next, use the point-slope formula of a line using the slope and the point (7,23). The formula is with the slope and the point is $y-y_1=m(x-x_1)$. The equation is $y-23=4(x-7)$. Distribute and solve for $y \times y-23=4x-28$; $y=4x-5$. Change the equation to function notation: $f(x)=4x-5$.
10	A	Begin by finding the slope of the line that contains the points. Use the points (14,31) and (16,49). The slope is $\frac{49-31}{16-14} = \frac{18}{2}$ =9. Next, use the point-slope formula of a line using the slope and the point (15,40). The formula is $y-y_1=m(x-x_1)$. With the slope and the point the equation is $y-40=9(x-15)$. Distribute and solve for $y \times y-40=9x-135$; $y=9x-95$. Change the equation to function notation: $f(x)=9x-95$.
11	A	Begin by finding the slope of the line that contains the points. Use the points (25,48) and (27,52). The slope is $\frac{52-48}{27-25} = \frac{4}{2}$ =2. Next, use the point-slope formula of a line using the slope and the point (26,50). The formula is $y-y_1=m(x-x_1)$. With the slope and the point the equation is $y-50=2(x-26)$. Distribute and solve for $y \times y-50=2x-52$; $y=2x-2$. Change the equation to function notation: $f(x)=2x-2$.
12	C	Begin by finding the slope of the line that contains the points. Use the points (6,2) and (8,14). The slope is $\frac{14-2}{8-6} = \frac{12}{2}$ =6. Next, use the point-slope formula of a line using the slope and the point (7,8). The formula is $y-y_1=m(x-x_1)$. With the slope and the point the equation is $y-8=6(x-7)$. Distribute and solve for $y \times y-8=6x-42$; $y=6x-34$. Change the equation to function notation: $f(x)=6x-34$.
13	B	Setup a proportion of guests to total number of people, $\frac{8}{5}=\frac{x}{576}$. Solve by cross multiplying. $8x=2880$. Divide both sides by 8. So $x=360$.
14	A	Student must recognize that $55 is the constant in the equation (flat fee).

Question No.	Answer	Detailed Explanation
15	C	Create an equation in which the number of production workers plus the number of support people add up to 480. The number of production workers is 12+18m where m is the number of months. The number of support people is 6+24m. The equation is 12+18m+6+24m=480. Begin by combining like terms on the left side of the equation: 18+42m=480. Next, subtract 18 from both sides and then divide both sides by 42. This gives you m=11. The factory will be fully staffed in 11 months.
16	B	Create an inequality that shows the ticket revenue is greater than the expenses. This inequality is 8x≥420+2x where x is the number of tickets. The first step to solve the inequality is subtracting 2x from both sides. This gives you 6x≥420. Divide both sides by and x≥70.The Council must sell 70 tickets to recover the costs of the facility.
17	B	Create two equations, one that determines how many minutes Drake will need to type his paper and the other one that determines how many minutes Heidi will need to type her paper. Drake's equation is 45m=2160 and Heidi's equation is 60m=2640. Solving each equation using division, you can see that Drake will take 48 minutes and Heidi will take 44 minutes. Together they will take 92 minutes of typing to finish both term papers.
18	C	Create an inequality that shows that the second courier service costs less than the first courier service. The second courier service costs 20+5p where p is the number of pounds. The first courier service costs 18+6p. The inequality is 20+5p<18+6p. Solve the inequality by subtracting 5p from both sides and subtracting 18 from both sides. This gives you p>2. Bryan is going to ship more than two pounds.
19	B	Student must apply inverse operations by multiplying both sides of the equation by 2 and then divide by h to isolate b.
20	D	Student must apply the inverse operations: begin by multiplying both sides of the equation by R to isolate E^2 and then take the square root of both sides of the equation to isolate E.
21	D	Student must solve for c by applying the inverse operation of subtraction to the terms a and b; the question also requires that the students recognize the formula can be written two ways, one using the distributive property, making answer choices a) and b) the same formula just expressed in different ways.

Question No.	Answer	Detailed Explanation
22	B	The question asks you to solve for r in the formula $7 = \frac{r}{7}(2s - 5t)$. First, multiply both sides of the formula by 7. This gives you $49 = r(2s - 5t)$. Next, divide both sides by 2s-5t. The result is $\frac{49}{2s - 5t}$.
23	D	The question asks you to solve for w in the formula $2u = \frac{w}{5}(7x - 3y)$. First, multiply both sides of the formula by 5. This gives you $10u = w(7x - 3y)$. Next, divide both sides by 7x-3y. The result is $w = \frac{10u}{7x - 3y}$.
24	C	The question asks you to solve for q in the formula $\frac{7r + 5s}{3q} = 8$. First, multiply both sides of the formula by 3q. This gives you $7r + 5s = 24q$. Next, divide both sides by 24. The result is $q = \frac{7r + 5s}{24}$.

Chapter 6 - Reasoning with Equations and Inequalities

Question No.	Answer	Detailed Explanation
1	B	The question asks you to find the solution to 8x−8=96. Begin by adding 8 to both sides of the equation. This gives you 8x=104. Next, divide both sides by 8 and x=13.
2	D	The only answer choice that holds true is d because of the commutative property of multiplication; the other equations are only true if a=b
3	D	The question asks you to find the solution to the equation $\frac{x}{5}$ - 11 = 2 . Begin by adding 11 to both sides of the equation. This gives you $\frac{x}{5}$=13. Next, multiply both sides by 5 and x=65.
4	A	Student must first solve the one-step equation by applying the inverse operations of addition and then division resulting in the inequality x<4 ; answer choice a shows the positive integers less than 4.
5	B	The question asks you to find the solutions to the quadratic equation $2x^2-3x+1=0$. Find the solutions using factoring. In factoring, you factor the first and the third term in such a way that the two factors add to give the middle term when checking the factoring using the FOIL process. Since the third term is positive, the two factors of that term must have the same sign. Since the second term is negative both of the factors must be negative. Thus, the factored equation is (2x−1)(x−1)=0. Find the solutions by making each factor equal to zero. 2x−1=0; x=½ and x−1=0; x=1.
6	A	This problem can be easily solved by rearranging the equation so that it is solved for zero and then factoring out the greatest common factor −8p and then solving for each factor as shown: $-8p^2=40p$ $-8p^2-40p=0$ $-8p(p+5)=0$ p=0 and p=−5

Question No.	Answer	Detailed Explanation
7	C	The elimination method (also known as the addition method) allows you to add the two equations together thereby eliminating one of the variables so that you can solve for the one that is left. Then use the one that you know to help you find the other one. $$5x+2y=0$$ $$3x-2y=-16$$ $$8x=-16$$ $$x=-2$$ Now use that x-value and plug back into one of the original two equations to find y. $$5x+2y=0$$ $$5(-2)+2y=0$$ $$-10+2y=0$$ $$2y=10$$ $$y=5$$ So then the final answer is $(-2, 5)$ or choice C.
8	C	The question asks you to solve the system of equations below by replacing one equation with the sum of the two equations or by a multiple of the equation, and then adding the two equations together. $$2x-3y=7$$ $$3x+y=5$$ Multiply the second equation by 3. $$2x-3y=7$$ $$9x+3y=15$$ Add the equations together to eliminate y and solve for x. $$11x=22$$ $$x=2$$ Substitute the value of x into one of the equations and solve for y. $$3(2)+y=5$$ $$6+y=5$$ $$y=-1$$ The solution to the system of equations is $(2,-1)$.

Question No.	Answer	Detailed Explanation
9	A	You can set up a system of equations to solve this problem. We will let p equal the cost of one can of paint and r equal the cost of one roller. The two equations would be set up as follows $2p + r = 62$ $5p + 2r = 151$ Now you can multiply the top equation by -2 to create r's that are opposites and would eliminate. $-2(2p + r = 62)$ $-4p - 2r = -124$ Now add this changed equation to the original bottom equation $-4p - 2r = -124$ $5p + 2r = 151$ $p = 27$ Now use the fact p=27 and one of the original equations to find r. $2p + r = 62$ $2(27) + r = 62$ $54 + r = 62$ $r = 8$ So the intersection point and final answer is (27, 8).
10	C	Convert each equation to slope-intercept form. The system becomes: $y = -3x + 4$ $y = 3x - 2$ For each equation, plot the y-intercept point, and use the slope to find another point on the line. Then, identify the point where the two lines intersect. The graph of this system of equations is below. Notice that the two lines intersect at the point (1,1).

Question No.	Answer	Detailed Explanation
11	B	To solve this system of equations, start by substituting ¼ x−8 or 0.25x - 8 in for y in the first equation like so, $y = x^2 + 5x + 9$ $0.25x - 8 = x^2 + 5x + 9$ $0 = x^2 + 4.75x + 17$ Now use the discriminant b^2-4ac to determine how many solutions this system would have. $4.75^2-4(1)(17)=-45.4375$ Since the discriminant is a negative number, there would be no real solutions and the two graphs would not intersect.
12	B	The question asks you to solve this system of a quadratic equation and a linear equation algebraically. $x^2+y^2=36$ $x=4$ Substitute 4 into the second equation for x and solve for y. $x^2+y^2=36$ $4^2+y^2=36$ $16+y^2=36$ $y^2=20$ $y=\pm2\sqrt{0}$
13	C	The question asks you to identify the function that contains the point (6,2). If you substitute x=6 into $f(x) = -\frac{3}{2}x + 11$, you get $f(6) = -\frac{3}{2}(6) + 11 = -9 + 11 = 2$. The other functions do not give the correct y−value.
14	A	The question asks you to find the point, in the first quadrant, where the functions $f(x)=x^2+8x-15$ and $g(x)=-x^2+4x+15$ intersect. Set the functions equal to each other and solve for x. Then substitute that answer into one of the functions to find y. $x^2+8x-15=-x^2+4x+15$; $2x^2+4x-30=0$; $x^2+2x-15=0$ Factor and solve this equation. $(x-3)(x+5)=0$; $x-3=0;x=3;x+5=0$; $x=-5$. Select x=3 to be in the first quadrant. $f(3)=3^2+8(3)-15=18$. The two curves intersect at the point (3,18).

Question No.	Answer	Detailed Explanation
15	D	You can see by the graph below that the intersection of the two lines happens between 2 and 3 days. You can also have your calculator tell you the intersection of the two lines pinpointing exactly when the two start to overlap. That happens when x≈2.7. So the overlap begins between day 2 and 3. The correct answer is then choice D.

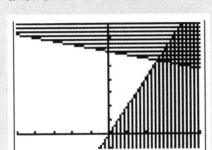

Chapter 7 - Interpreting Functions

Question No.	Answer	Detailed Explanation
1	B	The range is the list of all the y-values, most commonly given in numerical order. Answer choice B is the only one that lists every y-value in the table.
2	A	The question asks us to provide the range of $h(x)=x^2-9x-33$ on the domain $\{21,22,23,24\}$. The domain of a function is the set of input values into the function. The range of the function is the set of output values for the domain. This table shows the domain of $h(x)$ and the calculations of the range for each element of the domain.

Domain	Calculations	Range
21	$(21)^2-9(21)-33$	219
22	$(22)^2-9(22)-33$	253
23	$(23)^2-9(23)-33$	289
24	$(24)^2-9(24)-33$	327

Question No.	Answer	Detailed Explanation
3	B	The input variable is x. Cubing the input variable is a term x^3. Tripling that value is a term $3x^2$. Adding 9 is the term $+9$. Put together, we have $f(x)=x^3+9$. Therefore, $f(4)=4^3+9=64+9=73$.
4	C	The input will be the part in parenthesis beside the "f" and the output will be on the opposite side from this. The only choice that correctly states this is answer choice C.
5	A	A recursive formula uses the previous term to find the next term. In an arithmetic sequence, the recursive formula is: $a_n=a_{n-1}+d$, where n is the term number and d is the common difference between each term. The given sequence is an arithmetic sequence, where each term is 14 more than the previous term, so the common difference is 14. Therefore, to find the next term, add 14 to the previous term, giving a formula of: $a_n=a_{n-1}+14$

Question No.	Answer	Detailed Explanation
6	C	You could extend this sequence out to the 15th term, or you could find the function and evaluate it at 15 as shown here. The first term is 13, and the common difference -2, so that gives us the function $f(x) = 13 - 2(n-1)$. By plugging in a 15 for x we get $f(x) = 13 - 2(15-1) = 13 - 2(14) = 13 - 28 = -15$.
7	B	The scale of the graph for the dependent variable shows X 100. Thus, the graph shows that there were people at the event from 3 hours to 5 hours . If you look at the graph, you can see that the graph is horizontal at y = 200 from 3 hours to 5 hours, which means the number of people at the event was steady.
8	A	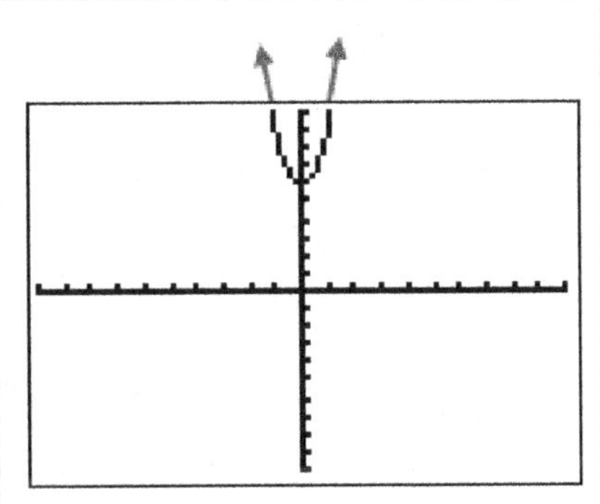 End behavior describes what is happening at the ends of a function. Disregard what is happening anywhere else. This graph looks as follows. Concentrate on the red arrows at the ends. As x heads to negative infinity on the left end, y is heading upward to positive infinity. As x heads to positive infinity on the right end, y is heading upward to positive infinity. Therefore answer choice A is correct.
9	D	The function is a polynomial function. The domain of all polynomial functions, in a mathematical context is $(-\infty, \infty)$. However, in a real world context, the domain must allow the function to obey the rules of the real world. The ball is hit at time equals 0 seconds, and the ball lands, according to the graph, at time equals 7 seconds. Therefore, the domain is [0,7].
10	C	You could add as much as you want to your savings so there will not be a maximum number as shown in answer A. The most you can subtract from a $500 savings is 500 dollars so the smallest number in the domain would be -500 with no maximum number leaving answer choice C as the correct answer.

Question No.	Answer	Detailed Explanation
11	B	Average rate of change is slope. The slope between two points (x_1, y_1) and (x_2, y_2) is calculated with the slope formula: $\frac{y_2 - y_1}{x_2 - x_1}$. In this problem, the two points are $(5, -7)$ and $(20, 26)$ so, using the formula, we have $\frac{26 - (-7)}{20 - 5} = \frac{33}{15} = \frac{11}{5}$.
12	D	First we need to find $g(-1)$ and $g(5)$. $$g(-1) = \frac{1}{2(-1)} - (-1)^2 = -1.5$$ $$g(5) = \frac{1}{2(5)} - (5)^2 = -24.9$$ Next we need to calculate the change in $g(x)$ divided by the change in x as shown below $$\frac{\triangle g(x)}{\triangle x} = \frac{-24.9 - (-1.5)}{5 - (-1)} = \frac{-23.4}{6} = -3.9$$
13	B	The parent square root curve has its beginning on the origin which is the point $(0,0)$ and has the equation $y = \sqrt{x}$. The graph in the figure has its beginning on the point $(3,1)$. This means the parent function is moved 3 units to the right and 1 unit upward, giving a new equation: $y = \sqrt{x-3} + 1$.
14	C	The question asks us to select a function that is equivalent to $h(x) = x^4 - 3x^3 - 4x^2$ and allows us to find the zeros of the given function. The terms in this function have a greatest common factor (GCF) of x^2. We can factor the GCF out of the function. Then, we can factor the resulting quadratic trinomial into linear factors, and still have an equivalent function: $$h(x) = x^4 - 3x^3 - 4x^2 = x^2(x^2 - 3x - 4) = x^2(x-4)(x+1)$$ Lastly, we can set each factor equal to zero to find the zeros of the function.
15	C	To calculate the rate of growth of the functions, we calculate their slope. The slope between two points (x_1, y_1) and (x_2, y_2) is calculated with the slope formula: $\frac{y_2 - y_1}{x_2 - x_1}$. In this problem, we estimate the slope of h(x) with the two points $(3,1)$ and $(9,9)$ so, using the formula, we have $\frac{9-1}{9-3} = \frac{8}{6} = \frac{4}{3}$. The function k(x) is a linear function in slope-intercept form y=mx+b. The slope of k(x) is 2. Therefore, k(x) has a faster growth rate at x=6.

Chapter 8 - Building Functions

Question No.	Answer	Detailed Explanation
1	D	The questions states that the relationship is expressed as ordered pairs (g,h). This means that h is the output of a function of g. The question states that the output is always 7 less than the square of the input variable. The input variable is g, the square of g is g^2, and 7 less than means subtract 7. Therefore, the function is $f(g)=g^2-7$.
2	C	The question states that a is the independent variable. Therefore, the function must be in terms of a giving you a function notation of f(a). Notice in the table that b is always 4 times a, so the function is $f(a)=4a$.
3	A	First we need to find the maximum value of t in the height function, $h(t)=-1.3t^2+5t$. We can use $t=\dfrac{-b}{2a}$ as shown below $$t=\dfrac{-(5)}{2(-1.3)}\approx1.92$$ Now to find the value of PE in terms of mg, we just plug in 1.92 for the t-value as shown, $$PE=mg(-1.3t^2+5t)$$ $$PE=mg(-1.3(1.92)^2+5(1.92))$$ $$PE=4.81mg$$
4	A	A headwind blows in the opposite direction the boat is traveling slowing the boat's speed down. A headwind takes away from the boat's speed so we pick the function with speed minus headwind.
5	B	The first year you will get $10, so you have to pick the function that has a function value of 10 when you plug in a 1 for n. This eliminates choices A and D as these both give a value of $12.50 when you plug in a 1 for n. To find the correct answer between B and C, we will need to plug in a 2. The second year you should get $12.50. The only one that gives you $12.50 when you plug in a 2 for n is answer choice B.

Question No.	Answer	Detailed Explanation
6	C	By plugging in values for the recursive function we find that this series is 0, 4, 8, 12, 16.... (remember f_1 was given to be 0). Now we can simply plug in values for n in each of the answer choices until one of them gives the same sequence of numbers as shown below Answer choice A gives 8, 12... when you plug in 1 and 2 for n so this is not the right answer choice. Answer choice B gives 4, 8... when you plug in 1 and 2 for n so this is not the right answer choice. Answer choice C gives 0, 4... when you plug in 1 and 2 so this is the right explicit function for this sequence.
7	A	Your cable bill will be increasing so you should pick a function with a plus sign instead of subtraction. This rules out C and D as answers. The increase is $5 per year, so the y should be beside the 5 in the equation. This rules out answer B, leaving A as the correct answer.
8	C	Since the previous term was given this is a simple plug in the value problem as shown below. $f(n)=2 \times f_{n-1}+3$ $f(9)=2 \times f_8+3$ $f(9)=2 \times 509+3=1021$
9	A	The value added to the function causes a vertical shift in the graph. Since 12 is 5 units larger than 7, the graph of g(x) is obtained by shifting f(x) 5 units up.

Question No.	Answer	Detailed Explanation
10	C	When functions are written in the form such as $f(x)=a(x-h)^2+k$, the values a, h, and k, each cause specific transformations to the function. a causes a vertical stretch if $\|a\|>1$ a causes a vertical shrink if $0<\|a\|<1$ a causes a reflection of the graph across the x-axis if $a<0$ h shifts the graph horizontally if h is positive, the graph is translated to the right if h is negative, the graph is translated to the left k shifts the graph vertically if $k>0$, the graph is translated up if $k<0$, the graph is translated down A function is even if $f(-x)=f(x)$. Even functions are symmetrical across the y-axis. An function is odd if $f(-x)=-f(x)$. Odd functions are symmetrical about the origin, not across either axis. According to our rules, since the h-value in f(x) is 3, that graph is shifted right 3 units. Since the h-value in g(x) is -3, that graph is shifted left 3 units.
11	C	A number multiplied in front of a function will either stretch or shrink the original function. A number greater than zero will stretch the graph and a number less than zero will shrink the graph.
12	D	There are 4 differences in the two functions given. The first is the negative in front. This will cause the new graph to reflect over the x-axis. The second is the number in front of the x^2 decreases causing a vertical shrink. The third is the -2 being applied to the x^2 which will shift the graph to the right 2. Then finally the +3 being added on at the end will shift the graph up 3. The only answer choice that lists all 4 of these changes is answer D.

Question No.	Answer	Detailed Explanation
13	C	Rule #1: To find the inverse of a relation:
		Example #1 f(x)={(1,2), (3,4), (−5,7)}. To find f−1(x), switch the x and y values in the ordered pairs. So $f^{-1}(x)$={(2,1), (4,3), (7,−5)}
		Example #2 When the function is in equation form such as f(x)=3x−−4 To find f−1(x) switch x and y and then solve for y.
		y = 3x -- 4
		x = 3y -- 4 Switch x and y.
		$y = \dfrac{x - 4}{3}$. Solve for y.
		Therefore $f^{-1}(x) = \dfrac{x - 4}{3}$
		According to Example #2, to find the inverse of a function, you switch the x and y values in the equation and solve for y.
14	A	If we switch the x and y in the function, we end up with $x = 3^y$. The only way to solve for y is to take the log. We know that $a = b^c$ means $\log_b a = c$. Using that same rule for this inverse function we end up with answer choice A.
15	A	The function intersects the x-axis at its line of symmetry x = 0. The domain of the original function correlates to the range of the inverse function. Since our inverse function is $f^{-1}(x) = \sqrt{x}$, and there's no value of x that will make $f^{-1}(x)$ less than 0, that means the domain of our original function should be all values greater than or equal to 0, or A.

Chapter 9 - Linear, Quadratic, and Exponential Models

Question No.	Answer	Detailed Explanation
1	C	The question states that one dollar is invested in an account that accumulates 20% interest per year. This means that the value of the account increases proportionally based on the amount in the account. The formula for this type of function is $f(x) = 1(1.2)^x$ which has a growth factor of 1.2 per year. A graph of this function is below.

2	A	The question states that the temperature began at 2°C and decreases 5°C each hour. This means that the beginning temperature is the y-intercept and the temperature decreases the same amount (5°C) each hour, which means the slope of the graph is -5. This situation can be represented by the linear function $f(x) = -5x + 2$. A table of values of this function is below.

x	-4	-3	-2	-1
y	22	17	12	7

3	C	An exponential function's interval difference will not be the same every time, but the factor by which it increases or decreases will be. Although exponential functions are known to grow quickly, this is not always the case.
4	A	The difference between the intervals in a linear function are always the same. If the differences between the intervals are increasing or decreasing you should suspect an exponential function.

Question No.	Answer	Detailed Explanation
5	A	The questions states that the sequence is arithmetic. The formula for an arithmetic sequence is $a_n = a_1 + d(n-1)$, where a_n is the nth term, a_1 is the first term, and d is the difference between each term. The table shows that $a_1 = 5$ and each term is 5 more than the previous term so d=5. Using these numbers, the sequence rule is $a_n = 5 + 5(n-1) = 5 + 5n - 5 = 5n$.
6	A	The values in the table do not reflect a linear relationship because the y-values are increasing at an increasing rate. They also do not reflect an exponential relationship because each y-value is not the previous y-value multiplied by a specific value number. A close look at the relationship between the x- and y- values reveals that the points are all in the form (x, x^2), so the function whose values are in the table is $f(x) = x^2$.
7	D	To be exponential, the exponent MUST be a variable. D is the only choice like this.
8	C	Since her resting heart rate is 60. The value of the function at 0 should be 60. Then after 1 minute the value should increase by 10 and so on. The correct function is C.
9	B	Because this is an exponential function it will eventually surpass the others because it is increasing at an ever-increasing rate. That means linear functions and polynomials will be no match for it.
10	B	Linear functions will have an x to the first power. There will be no variables in the exponent and no x to the second power.
11	A	A quadratic function is a second degree polynomial because of the x to the second power, making it a variation of a polynomial function.
12	B	You can see from the graph that the purple graph surpasses the linear graph only when x is less than -5

Question No.	Answer	Detailed Explanation
13	B	The number of widgets in the warehouse is calculated by subtracting the number of widgets sold from the beginning inventory of widgets. The problem states that the warehouse has 950 widgets when the business opened. The number of widgets sold is calculated by multiplying the sales per week by the number of weeks. The problem also states that the business expects to sell 45 widgets every week and the variable w represents the number of weeks. Therefore, the function that represents the number of widgets in the warehouse after w weeks is $I(w)=950-45w$.
14	C	Net profit is the result of subtracting the expenses from the total revenue. The problem says the theater spent $565 to produce the play, so expenses total $565. The revenue is the price of each ticket times the number of tickets sold, so the total revenue is $35t$. Therefore, the function that represents total revenue minus expenses or net profit is $P(t)=35t-565$.
15	B	The number of students at the school is calculated by adding the number of students who were at the school in the beginning to the number of new students. The problem states that the school started with 64 students. The number of additional students is calculated by multiplying the number of new students per year by the number of years. The problem also states that the school expects to enroll 26 students every year and the variable x represents the number of years. Therefore, the function that represents the number of students at the school after x years is $S(x)=64+26x$.

Chapter 10 - Interpreting Categorical and Quantitative Data

Question No.	Answer	Detailed Explanation
1	C	If we rearrange the data set in the question in numerical order, we have this set. {3,3,3,4,4,5,5,5,5,6,6,6,7,7,8,8,8} Therefore, the line plot must contain three 3's, two 4's, four 5's, three 6's, two 7's, and three 8's. The dot plot below contains the correct numbers.
2	B	Consider each option. Option A -- There are no data points in the 60 column, this statement is false. Option B -- The 90 column has more data points than any other column therefore most students scored 90. This option is correct. Option C-- Since no students scored 60 this would be the score with the fewest student scores. Option C is incorrect. Option D -- There were 2 students scoring 70 and 5 students scoring 80 for a total of 7 students. There are 7 data points in the 90 column as well meaning there were equal number of students scoring either 70 or 80 and students scoring 90. Option D is not correct.

Question No.	Answer	Detailed Explanation
3	C	Consider each of the options

Option A -- Box Plot -- A box plot is best used to represent numerical data from a single event such as test scores or race times. It would not work as well for showing how many students own each type of pet.

Option B -- Histogram -- A histogram is used to show ranges of data for single events much like a box plot, but in a different form.

Option C -- A dot plot is a like a bar graph and could easily show how many students own each type of pet.

Option D -- Since the dot plot works best, All of the above would not be the best choice. |
| 4 | C | The question asks us to provide the difference between the medians of two sets of numbers. We find a median by arranging the numbers in the set from the least to the greatest. The median is the middle number. First, we will find the median of set A: {6,8,10,12,14,16,18,20,22}. The numbers are already in order from least to greatest. Notice that the set has 9 numbers, so the middle number is the fifth number, which is 14. Next, we will find the median of set B: {3,5,7,9,11,13,15,17,19}. The numbers are, again, already in order from least to greatest. Notice that the set also has 9 numbers, so the middle number is also the fifth number, which is 11. The difference between the two medians is 3. |
| 5 | C | The upper quartile will be the score for which 25% of the class scored better and 75% of the class scores lower.
Place the data in numerical order.

| 71 | 75 | 79 | 81 | 82 | 85 | 86 | 87 | 92 | 95 | 99 | 100 |
There are 12 scores so there need to be 9 scores lower and 3 scores higher. The upper quartile will lie between 92 and 95.

| 71 | 75 | 79 | 81 | 82 | 85 | 86 | 87 | 92 | 95 | 99 | 100 |
Take the average of the two numbers to find the upper quartile.
$$\frac{92 + 95}{2} = \frac{187}{2} = 93.5$$ |

Question No.	Answer	Detailed Explanation
6	C	A data set that is distributed normally has the unique characteristic that the mean is the same as the median. The figure below shows a normal distribution. Notice that the distribution is symmetric about a center. This center is both the mean and the median. 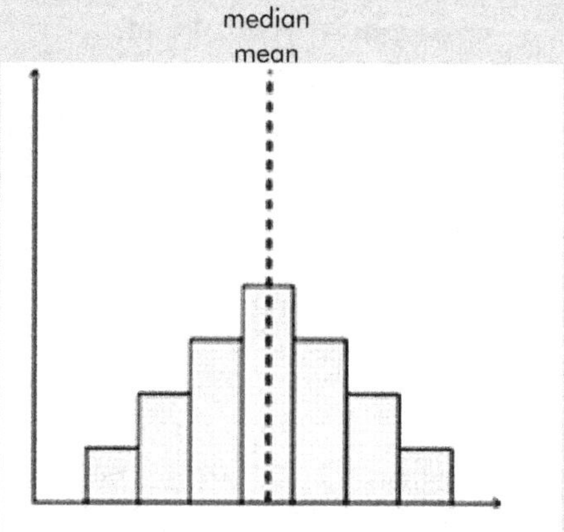
7	D	When the data has a mean and median that are equal then the data must be symmetrical -- it will not be skewed. The data may also be a mound, but it does not have to a mound. Therefore D is the best answer.
8	C	The two-way table shows how many students, sorted by grade, prefer each pet. If we are given that the student is a 10th, we need to only look at the 10th grade row. We can see that 21 out of 51 10th graders prefer a cat. This ratio reduces to $\frac{7}{17}$.
9	C	Note that all of the choices other than D are represented in numbers. However there is no way to numerically represent a color. This is referred to as categorical data.
10	C	Notice that the graph increases to a point then return downward. This "U" shape whether open at the top or bottom is characteristic of Quadratic functions.
11	B	In equations with dependent and independent variables "x" typically serves to represent the independent variable. In Dr. Winthrop's study the temperature is the independent variable. The variable "x" represents temperature.

Question No.	Answer	Detailed Explanation
12	B	We will write the equation in slope-intercept form, $y=mx+b$, which gives us the length of the candle after burning for x hours. The question states that John starts with a 10cm candle, which is equivalent to a y−intercept point (0,10). This means that we now have $y=mx+10$. The question also states that after three hours, the candle is 8cm long, which is equivalent to the point (3,8). Now, we will use the point and substitute the x and y from the point into the equation to find the slope: $y=mx+10$; $8=m(3)+10$; $-2=3m$; $m=-\frac{2}{3}$. The equation is $y=-\frac{2}{3}x+10$, with a slope of $-\frac{2}{3}$. The slope represents the rate in number of centimeters the candle burns every hour. It is negative because the length of the candle is decreasing.
13	C	The intercept is where the function crosses the y-axis or where x=0. The variable "x" is the independent variable so Option C is the best choice.
14	A	Eating ice cream does not turn people violent nor does it cause them to murder someone else. Therefore, the relationship between ice cream sales and the violent crime rate is a correlation, even though one event has nothing to do with the other event.
15	A	People associate with each other everywhere, in the home, in restaurants, in stores, parks, public transportation; the list goes on and on. Closing the schools did not stop people from associating with each other in other locations. It is likely that the spread of the swine flu had run its course by the time the decision was made to close schools. Therefore, the relationship between closing the schools and the spread of swine flu is a correlation.

What will Algebra 1 Assessment Look Like?

In many ways, the Algebra 1 assessments will be unlike anything many students have ever seen. The tests require students to complete tasks to assess a deeper understanding of the CCSS in domains such as Number and Quantity, Algebra, Functions and Statistics & probability.

Is it necessary to take the Algebra 1 before taking up Geometry?

The students can decide their preferred High School credit program based on their future college graduation choices. However, it is recommended to take either Algebra 1 or Integrated Math 1 first before choosing other High School math programs as this helps the students to master the basic skills.

What are the Math credit programs offered in High Schools?

Most of the High Schools offer Algebra 1, Algebra 2, Geometry, Integrated Math 1 and Integrated Math 2.

What item types are included in the Online Algebra 1 Test?

Because the assessment is online, the test will consist of a combination of new types of questions:

1. Drag and Drop
2. Drop Down
3. Essay Response
4. Extended Constructed Response
5. Hot Text Select and Drag
6. Hot Text Selective Highlight
7. Matching Table In-line
8. Matching Table Single Response
9. Multiple Choice – Single Correct Response, radial buttons
10. Multiple Choice – Multiple Response, checkboxes
11. Numeric Response
12. Short Text
13. Table Fill-in

What if I buy more than one Lumos Study Program?

Step 1

Visit the URL and login to your account.
http://www.lumoslearning.com

Step 2

Click on 'My tedBooks' under the "Account" tab.
Place the Book Access Code and submit.

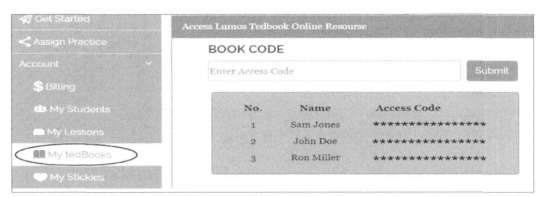

Step 3

To add the new book for a registered student, choose the
○ Existing Student button and select the student and submit.

Assign To ⊕

◉ Existing Student   ○ Add New student

○ Sam Jones

○ John Doe

○ Ron Miller

Submit

To add the new book for a new student, choose the ○ Add New student
button and complete the student registration.

Assign To ⊕

○ Existing Student   ◉ Add New student

Register Your TedBook

Student Name:*   Enter First Name   Enter Last Name

Student Login*

Password*

Submit

Lumos StepUp® Mobile App FAQ For Students

What is the Lumos StepUp® App?

It is a FREE application you can download onto your Android Smartphones, tablets, iPhones, and iPads.

What are the Benefits of the StepUp® App?

This mobile application gives convenient access to Practice Tests, Common Core State Standards, Online Workbooks, and learning resources through your Smartphone and tablet computers.

- Eleven Technology enhanced question types in both MATH and ELA
- Sample questions for Arithmetic drills
- Standard specific sample questions
- Instant access to the Common Core State Standards
- Jokes and cartoons to make learning fun!

Do I Need the StepUp® App to Access Online Workbooks?

No, you can access Lumos StepUp® Online Workbooks through a personal computer. The StepUp® app simply enhances your learning experience and allows you to conveniently access StepUp® Online Workbooks and additional resources through your smart phone or tablet.

How can I Download the App?

Visit **lumoslearning.com/a/stepup-app** using your Smartphone or tablet and follow the instructions to download the app.

QR Code
for Smartphone
Or Tablet Users

Lumos StepUp® Mobile App FAQ
For Parents and Teachers

What is the Lumos StepUp® App?

It is a free app that teachers can use to easily access real-time student activity information as well as assign learning resources to students. Parents can also use it to easily access school-related information such as homework assigned by teachers and PTA meetings. It can be downloaded onto smart phones and tablets from popular App Stores.

What are the Benefits of the Lumos StepUp® App?

It provides convenient access to

- Standards aligned learning resources for your students
- An easy to use Dashboard
- Student progress reports
- Active and inactive students in your classroom
- Professional development information
- Educational Blogs

How can I Download the App?

Visit **lumoslearning.com/a/stepup-app** using your Smartphone or tablet and follow the instructions to download the app.

**QR Code
for Smartphone
Or Tablet Users**

Progress Chart

Standard	Lesson	Q No.	Page No.	Practice		Mastered	Re-practice /Reteach
				Date	Score		
	Chapter 1: Real Numbers		47				
N.RN.1	Evaluating Rational Exponents	1					
		2					
		3					
		4					
		5					
N.RN.2	Simplifying Expressions with Rational Exponents	6					
		7					
		8					
		9					
		10					
N.RN.3	Simplifying Irrational Expressions	11					
		12					
		13					
		14					
		15					
	Chapter 2: Quantities		50				
N.Q.1	Understanding Units of Measure & Unit Conversion	1					
		2					
		3					
		4					
		5					
N.Q.2	Recognizing Reasonable Answers to Word Problems	6					
		7					
		8					
		9					
		10					
N.Q.3	Choosing an Appropriate Level of Accuracy for Measurements	11					
		12					
		13					

Standard	Lesson	Q No.	Page No.	Practice		Mastered	Re-practice /Reteach
				Date	Score		
		14					
		15					
	Chapter 3: Seeing Structure in Expressions		**54**				
A-SSE.1a A-SSE.1b	Interpret parts of an Expression	1					
		2					
		3					
		4					
		5					
A.SSE.2	Rewriting Expressions:	6					
		7					
		8					
		9					
		10					
A.SSE.3a A.SSE.3b A.SSE.3c	Writing Expressions in Equivalent Forms	11					
		12					
		13					
		14					
		15					
	Chapter 4: Arithmetic with Polynomials		**57**				
A.APR.1	Understand Polynomials	1					
		2					
		3					
		4					
		5					
		6					
	Chapter 5: Creating Equations		59				
A.CED.1	Creating Equations to Describe Numbers or Relationships	1					
		2					
		3					
		4					

Standard	Lesson	Q No.	Page No.	Practice		Mastered	Re-practice /Reteach
				Date	Score		
		5					
		6					
A.CED.2	Creating Equations in Two or More Variables	7					
		8					
		9					
		10					
		11					
		12					
A.CED.3	Systems of Linear Equations and Inequalities	13					
		14					
		15					
		16					
		17					
		18					
A.CED.4	Rearrange formulas to highlight a quantity of interest	19					
		20					
		21					
		22					
		23					
		24					
	Chapter 6: Reasoning with Equations and Inequalities		65				
A.REI.1	Explaining Equation and using properties	1					
		2					
A.REI.3	Solve linear equations and in-equalities in one variable	3					
		4					
A.REI.4a A.REI.4b	Solve quadratic equations in one variable.	5					
		6					
A.REI.5	Solving Systems of Equations in Two Variables	7					

Standard	Lesson	Q No.	Page No.	Practice		Mastered	Re-practice /Reteach
				Date	Score		
		8					
A.REI.6	Solve Systems of Equations Exactly and Approximately	9					
		10					
A.REI.7	Solve Simple Systems Consisting of a Linear Equation and a Quadratic Equation	11					
		12					
A.REI.10	Understanding the Relationship between Equations & Graphs	13					
A.REI.11	Reasoning with Equations and Graphs	14					
A.REI.12	Reasoning with Equations and Inequalities	15					
	Chapter 7: Interpreting Functions		**69**				
F.IF.1	Understanding Functions, Domain, and Range	1					
		2					
F.IF.2	Using Function Notation & Evaluating Functions	3					
		4					
F.IF.3	Recognizing that Sequences are Functions	5					
		6					
F.IF.4	Modeling Functional Relationships with Tables and Graphs	7					
		8					
F.IF.5	Relating Domain of a Function to its Graph	9					
		10					
F.IF.6	Calculating and Interpreting Rate of Change	11					
		12					

Standard	Lesson	Q No.	Page No.	Practice		Mastered	Re-practice /Reteach
				Date	Score		
F.IF.7a F.IF.7e	Understanding the Graph of a Function	13					
F.IF.8a F.IF.8b	Writing Functions in Different Forms to find Critical Information	14					
F.IF.9	Comparing properties of Functions	15					
	Chapter 8: Building functions		**74**				
F.BF.1b	Writing Functions that Describe a Relationship Between Two Quantities	1					
		2					
		3					
		4					
F.BF.2	Writing Arithmetic and Geometric Sequences	5					
		6					
		7					
		8					
F.BF.3	Transformation of Functions	9					
		10					
		11					
		12					
F.BF.4a	Finding Inverse Functions	13					
		14					
		15					
	Chapter 9: Linear, Quadratic, and Exponential Models		**78**				
F-LE.1a F-LE.1b F-LE.1c	Modeling Linear and Exponential Functions	1					
		2					
		3					
		4					
F-LE.2	Construct Linear and Exponential Functions	5					
		6					
		7					

Standard	Lesson	Q No.	Page No.	Practice		Mastered	Re-practice /Reteach
				Date	Score		
F-LE.3	Observing Exponential Graphs and Tables	9					
		10					
		11					
		12					
F-LE.5	Linear Equations in Business	13					
		14					
		15					
	Chapter 10: Interpreting Categorical and Quantitative Data		**81**				
S.ID.1	Representing data in graphical form	1					
		2					
		3					
S.ID.2	Using Statistics to compare data	4					
		5					
S.ID.3	Shape, Center and Outliers	6					
		7					
S.ID.5	Two way frequency tables	8					
		9					
S.ID.6a S.ID.6c	Scatter plots	10					
		11					
S.ID.7	Interpret the slope and the intercept	12					
		13					
S.ID.9	Distinguish between correlation and causation	14					
		15					

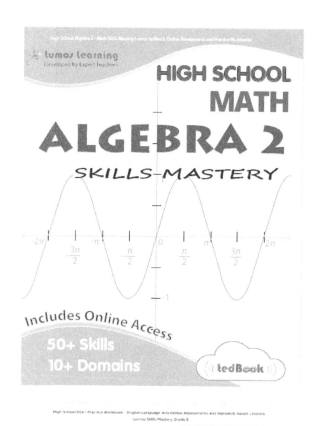

High School Algebra 2 - Math Skills Mastery Lumos tedBook Online Assessments and Practice Workbooks

Lumos Learning
Developed by Expert Teachers

HIGH SCHOOL
MATH
ALGEBRA 2
SKILLS-MASTERY

Includes Online Access

50+ Skills
10+ Domains

tedBook

High School Geometry - Math Skills Mastery Lumos tedBook Online Assessments and Practice Workbooks

Lumos Learning
Developed by Expert Teachers

HIGH SCHOOL
MATH
GEOMETRY
SKILLS MASTERY

Includes Online Access

44+ Skills
Four Category

tedBook

$$x^2 = y^2 + z^2$$

High School ELA 1 Practice Workbook - English Language Arts Online Assessments and Standards-based Lessons
Lumos Skills Mastery Grade 2

Lumos Learning
Developed by Expert Teachers

HIGH SCHOOL

English Language Arts (ELA) 1
tedBook

2 Practice Tests
30+ Topic-Based Lessons
1000+ Skills Mastery Questions
Smart Test Prep Methodology

INCLUDES ONLINE ACCESS

High School ELA 2 Practice Workbook - English Language Arts Online Assessments and Standards-based Lessons
Lumos Skills Mastery Grade 1-8

Lumos Learning
Developed by Expert Teachers

HIGH SCHOOL

English Language Arts (ELA) 2
tedBook

2 Practice Tests
30+ Topic-Based Lessons
1000+ Skills Mastery Questions
Smart Test Prep Methodology

INCLUDES ONLINE ACCESS

Available

- At Leading book stores
- Online www.LumosLearning.com

66797925R00077